Language 4
Fundamentals

Writing: Bonnie Brook
Communications
Content Editing: Marilyn Evans
Leslie Sorg
Copy Editing: Sonny Bennett
Art Direction: Cheryl Puckett
Cover Design: Liliana Potigian
Illustration: Mary Rojas
Design/Production: Carolina Caird
Arynne Elfenbein

EMC 2754

Evan-Moor®
Helping Children Learn

Visit
teaching-standards.com
to view a correlation
of this book.
This is a free service.

***Correlated to State and
Common Core State Standards***

**Congratulations on your purchase of some of the
finest teaching materials in the world.**

*Photocopying the pages in this book
is permitted for <u>single-classroom use only</u>.
Making photocopies for additional classes
or schools is prohibited.*

For information about other Evan-Moor products, call 1-800-777-4362,
fax 1-800-777-4332, or visit our Web site, www.evan-moor.com.
Entire contents © 2007 EVAN-MOOR CORP.
18 Lower Ragsdale Drive, Monterey, CA 93940-5746. Printed in USA.

CPSIA: Bang Printing, 28210 N. Avenue Stanford, Valencia, CA 91355 [7/2015]

Table of Contents

Language Fundamentals • EMC 2754 • © Evan-Moor Corp.

Usage

Vocabulary

Paragraph Editing

Answer Key

What's in *Language Fundamentals*?

Language Fundamentals is your comprehensive resource for grade-level grammar, mechanics, usage, and vocabulary practice. The broad scope of language skills and the range in difficulty of the activity pages enable you to precisely target those skills that each student needs to practice.

Targeted Skill Practice

The core of *Language Fundamentals* is the 160-plus pages of student-friendly skill activities.

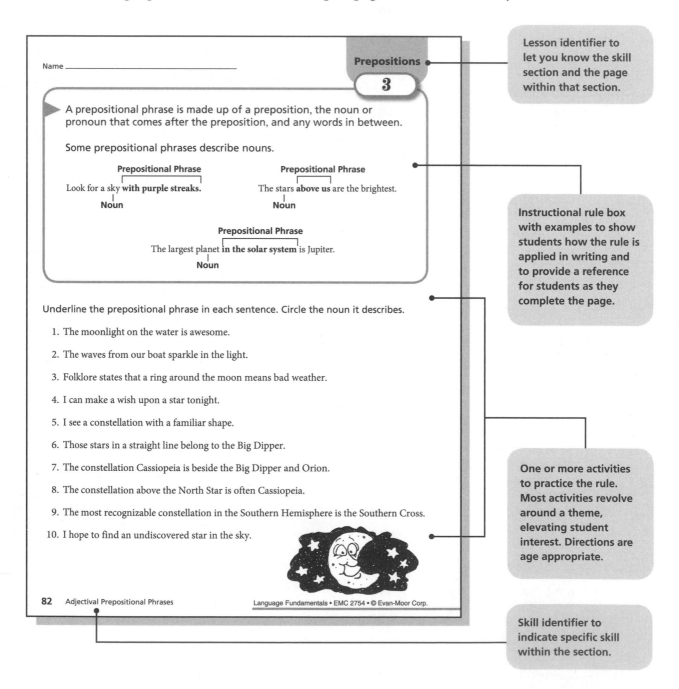

Name _____

Prepositions

3

A prepositional phrase is made up of a preposition, the noun or pronoun that comes after the preposition, and any words in between.

Some prepositional phrases describe nouns.

Prepositional Phrase
Look for a sky **with purple streaks.**
Noun

Prepositional Phrase
The stars **above us** are the brightest.
Noun

Prepositional Phrase
The largest planet **in the solar system** is Jupiter.
Noun

Underline the prepositional phrase in each sentence. Circle the noun it describes.

1. The moonlight on the water is awesome.

2. The waves from our boat sparkle in the light.

3. Folklore states that a ring around the moon means bad weather.

4. I can make a wish upon a star tonight.

5. I see a constellation with a familiar shape.

6. Those stars in a straight line belong to the Big Dipper.

7. The constellation Cassiopeia is beside the Big Dipper and Orion.

8. The constellation above the North Star is often Cassiopeia.

9. The most recognizable constellation in the Southern Hemisphere is the Southern Cross.

10. I hope to find an undiscovered star in the sky.

82 Adjectival Prepositional Phrases

Language Fundamentals • EMC 2754 • © Evan-Moor Corp.

Lesson identifier to let you know the skill section and the page within that section.

Instructional rule box with examples to show students how the rule is applied in writing and to provide a reference for students as they complete the page.

One or more activities to practice the rule. Most activities revolve around a theme, elevating student interest. Directions are age appropriate.

Skill identifier to indicate specific skill within the section.

Review Pages

There are 33 review pages presented in multiple-choice test format to provide test-prep practice. Each review covers a small subset of skills and may be used as an assessment of student skill acquisition.

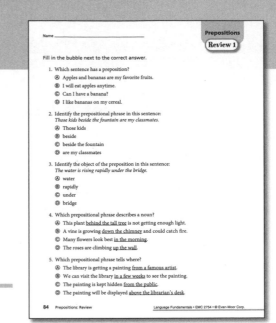

Paragraph Editing

These pages provide students with an opportunity to edit and correct paragraphs containing errors commonly made at this grade level. Each page is tied to specific skills addressed in the Targeted Skill Practice pages. After practicing a skill, students can use the corresponding pages in this section to transfer the skill to the context of writing.

A reproducible chart of proofreading marks is provided on page 194. Students can refer to this chart when editing those pages that direct students to use proofreading marks.

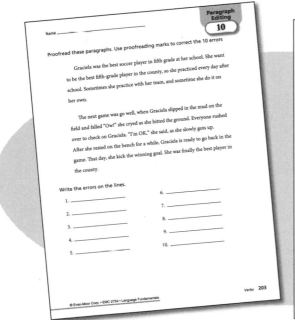

As a supplement to your core language arts program

What if...

- you've finished the material on a particular skill in your core program and your students still don't seem to get it?

- there is an objective in your state's standards that is not covered in the core program?

- you need homework materials to reinforce the core program lessons?

- you have a new student who missed a number of vital language lessons?

- you want to provide a resource teacher, after-school program, or tutor with language practice that connects with class work?

- you want to provide ongoing test-prep exercises as you move through your language program?

> *Language Fundamentals* can meet all these needs.

As an at-the-ready resource for those teachable moments

What if...

- you consistently overhear students using *good* and *bad* as adverbs?

- you've begun the revision stage of the writing process with your class and notice that your students do not vary their sentence structures?

- your students are confused as to when to use a comma with dependent and independent clauses?

- several of your students submit book reports with errors in capitalization and punctuation of titles?

> *Language Fundamentals* provides practice to address these skill needs.

As the perfect companion to Evan-Moor's *Daily Language Review*

Thousands of grade 1 through 6 classrooms use *Daily Language Review* for focused practice and review. Multiple studies show that this type of distributed, or spaced, practice is a powerful strategy for achieving proficiency and retention of skills.

Student responses on the weekly *Daily Language Review* units will indicate those skills needing further reinforcement. *Language Fundamentals* can then be used to provide the reteaching and additional practice. For example:

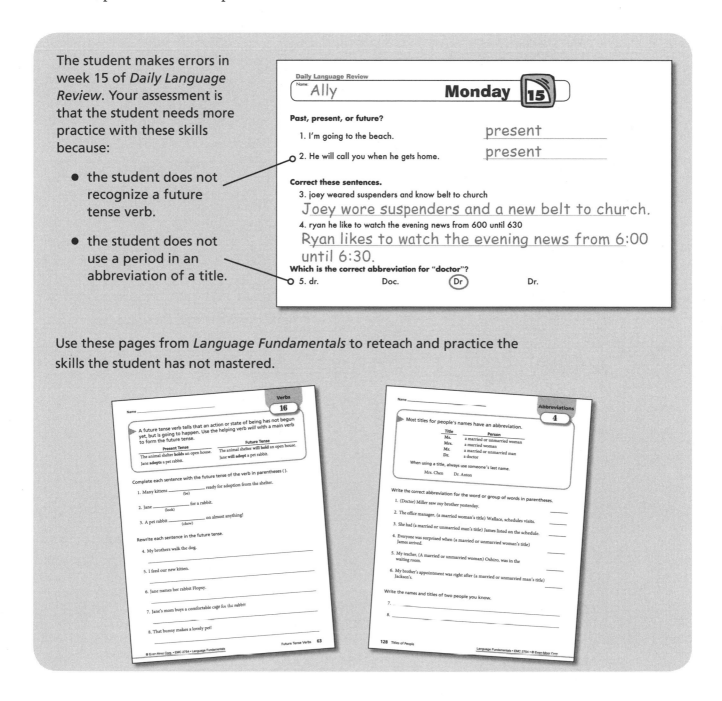

The student makes errors in week 15 of *Daily Language Review*. Your assessment is that the student needs more practice with these skills because:

- the student does not recognize a future tense verb.

- the student does not use a period in an abbreviation of a title.

Daily Language Review

Name: Ally

Monday 15

Past, present, or future?

1. I'm going to the beach. present

2. He will call you when he gets home. present

Correct these sentences.

3. joey weared suspenders and know belt to church

Joey wore suspenders and a new belt to church.

4. ryan he like to watch the evening news from 600 until 630

Ryan likes to watch the evening news from 6:00 until 6:30.

Which is the correct abbreviation for "doctor"?

5. dr.   Doc.   Dr   Dr.

Use these pages from *Language Fundamentals* to reteach and practice the skills the student has not mastered.

A noun is a word that names a person, place, or thing.

Types of Nouns	Examples
A noun can be a person.	boy, girl, friend, teacher, doctor, mechanic
A noun can be a place.	state, town, school, ocean, lake, beach
A noun can be a thing.	animal, tree, rock, shoe, bicycle, breakfast

Underline all the nouns in the sentences. Write *person, place,* or *thing* below each noun.

1. We are going to a big island to visit our aunt.

2. We will take a boat to get to the town where she lives.

3. My mother wants to go to a museum to see a famous painting.

4. I will watch a ballgame with my brother and my cousin.

5. I have money to buy a hat and a raincoat from a store.

6. My aunt will take us to the boardwalk to ride the roller coaster.

7. We will go to the theater to see a play.

8. I hope I see a celebrity in a restaurant so I can get an autograph!

Name _____

A noun can be singular or plural. Add *s* to most nouns to make them plural.

Singular	Plural
grandfather	grandfathers
orchard	orchards
apple	apples

Circle the singular nouns. Underline the plural nouns.

1. Most stores that sell animals stick to easy pets.

2. Most kids want a cat or dog as a furry friend.

3. Dogs are happy to play in the park or run on the beach.

4. Cats are happy to just hide under blankets or curl up in a chair.

5. Some parents prefer pets that live in cages, such as birds and hamsters.

6. A bird will twitter and sing as long as it has seeds to eat.

7. A hamster likes to run on its wheel.

8. I am always surprised to meet individuals with unusual creatures.

9. Imagine having a giant snake in your house.

10. Imagine having a rare insect that eats special plants.

11. Imagine having a horse or goats that need a barn to live in.

12. Imagine having a reptile that changes colors.

Name _____

> Add *es* to singular nouns that end in *sh, ch, x, s,* and *z*
> to form the plural.
>
> | Singular | Plural |
> |----------|--------|
> | bush | bush**es** |
> | church | church**es** |
> | tax | tax**es** |
> | class | class**es** |
> | waltz | waltz**es** |

Complete each sentence with the plural form of a word from the word box.

> klutz   box   wish   dress   sandwich
> boss   patch   fox   glass   toothbrush

1. We have many _____ of things to pack.

2. We have plates, _____, and silverware to pack.

3. We sometimes act like _____, but let's not break anything today!

4. We can pack our own clothing, such as shirts, pants, and _____.

5. Let's throw away clothes that are ripped or have _____.

6. Don't pack things we will need tonight, such as our _____.

7. Please make some _____ to eat on the long drive.

8. Don't forget the travel games and the baby's favorite book about _____.

9. We are packing because our mom's _____ offered her a new job.

10. She followed their _____, and now we are moving to another state.

To form the plural of nouns that end in a consonant and *y*, change the *y* to *i* and add *es*.

Singular	Plural
family	famil**ies**
story	stor**ies**

If a noun ends in a vowel and *y*, just add *s*.

Singular	Plural
monkey	monkey**s**
day	day**s**

Answer each clue with the plural form of a word from the word box.

fly	berry	donkey	play
baby	city	birthday	bunny

1. Live performances on stage _____

2. Blue, black, or red fruits _____

3. Bothersome insects _____

4. They come with cake and presents _____

5. Small and stubborn beasts of burden _____

6. Sometimes rabbits are called this _____

7. Humans and animals all start out as these _____

8. Los Angeles and New York are the largest _____

Language Fundamentals • EMC 2754 • © Evan-Moor Corp.

Some nouns have irregular plural forms. Practice these nouns and learn their spellings.

Singular Noun	Irregular Plural
mouse	**mice**
goose	**geese**
ox	**oxen**
tooth	**teeth**
child	**children**
woman	**women**
man	**men**

Read each sentence. Circle *Correct* if the sentence is correct. Circle *Incorrect* if it is incorrect. Rewrite each incorrect sentence correctly on the line below it.

1. There are many child watching the parade today.   Correct   Incorrect

_____

2. Everyone loves that float with the huge mouse on it.   Correct   Incorrect

_____

3. There are live goose in cages on the wagon.   Correct   Incorrect

_____

4. Suddenly, a group of woman screamed.   Correct   Incorrect

_____

5. Two real mouse skittered across the street.   Correct   Incorrect

_____

> Some nouns have the same spelling in both the singular and the plural form. Use context clues to tell if the nouns are singular or plural.
>
> **sheep   deer   moose   oxen   fish   trout   aircraft**
>
> I saw a **moose** on my trip to Canada.
>
> There are two **moose** along the road.

Underline the irregular noun in each sentence. Circle *Singular* or *Plural* to tell how it is used.

1. We are taking a small aircraft to get to the camp.   Singular   Plural

2. There is a stream where we will catch many fish.   Singular   Plural

3. I hope I get some trout.   Singular   Plural

4. We should see many deer in the woods.   Singular   Plural

5. I saw a mother deer and a fawn last year.   Singular   Plural

6. There is a ranch nearby with a dozen oxen.   Singular   Plural

7. Last year the boy on the ranch had a sheep.   Singular   Plural

8. This year the boy is caring for a young moose.   Singular   Plural

9. My father says moose don't make good pets.   Singular   Plural

10. My dad's idea of a great pet is a fish!   Singular   Plural

Fill in the bubble next to the correct answer.

1. Which sentence has nouns that name a person, a place, and a thing?
   - Ⓐ An actor is visiting a small restaurant.
   - Ⓑ The actor is starring in a new play tonight.
   - Ⓒ The actor is eating a meal in the restaurant.
   - Ⓓ The actor is signing autographs.

2. Which sentence has all plural nouns?
   - Ⓐ The players are in their uniforms.
   - Ⓑ The coaches are ready to begin the game.
   - Ⓒ The fans beside the field must find their seats.
   - Ⓓ The umpire yells for the game to begin.

3. Which sentence has a plural noun formed correctly with *es?*
   - Ⓐ There were trayes of food before the movie.
   - Ⓑ There were sandwiches for everyone.
   - Ⓒ There were many kinds of drinkes.
   - Ⓓ There were snackes after the movie, too.

4. Which sentence has the correct plural form of *party?*
   - Ⓐ We are planning two holiday partes this year.
   - Ⓑ One party is for friends and one is for family.
   - Ⓒ Both partyies will be in the backyard at our house.
   - Ⓓ We expect many friends to come to the parties.

5. Which sentence has the correct plural form of *ox* and *child?*
   - Ⓐ There are some ox in the zoo for children.
   - Ⓑ The children cannot pet these oxen.
   - Ⓒ The oxes could hurt the children.
   - Ⓓ The childs can watch the oxen from behind the fence.

A possessive noun shows belonging. For singular nouns, add an apostrophe and *s* (*'s*) to make the noun possessive.

Singular Noun	Singular Possessive	Example
mother	mother's	mother's baby
cat	cat's	cat's tail
book	book's	book's title
country	country's	country's leader

Read the sentences. Underline the possessive nouns. Circle any nouns that should be possessive. Write those nouns correctly on the lines.

1. Our teacher's friend is a famous author.   _____

2. The author's new book is on display in the library.   _____

3. The librarian said the writer visit is next week.   _____

4. Our class turn reviewing the book is tomorrow.   _____

5. Kids who have read it say the story's plot is exciting.   _____

6. I hear the book ending is very surprising.   _____

7. My friend favorite character is the detective.   _____

8. The detective role is important in the book.   _____

9. I would like to study the artist's pictures.   _____

10. I hear one picture clues can solve the mystery!   _____

Name _____

> A possessive noun can be singular or plural. For plural nouns that end in *s*, add an apostrophe after the *s* (*s'*).

Plural Noun	Plural Possessive	Example
coaches	coaches'	coaches' rules
dogs	dogs'	dogs' leashes
pianos	pianos'	pianos' keys
cities	cities'	cities' firefighters

Complete each sentence using the possessive form of a word from the word box.

> | | | | |
> |---|---|---|---|
> | singers | actors | songs | classes |
> | winners | judges | plays | bands |

1. The _____ voices are all good.

2. The _____ lyrics have been learned.

3. The _____ costumes have been made.

4. The _____ instruments have been tuned.

5. The _____ programs are printed.

6. The _____ prizes are ready.

7. The _____ rules have been decided on.

8. The _____ performances can begin!

Plural Possessive Nouns   **19**

Name _____

> Nouns can be common or proper.
>
> - A common noun is not specific and is not capitalized.
>
>   We will meet at a **mall**.
>
> - A proper noun tells specific information and is always capitalized.
>
>   We will meet at the **River Avenue Mall**.

Write a new sentence on each line. Change the underlined common noun to a proper noun.

1. Let's visit <u>a city</u> this summer.

   _____

2. We can eat at <u>a restaurant</u> that serves delicious food.

   _____

3. We can go to a concert to hear <u>a musical group.</u>

   _____

4. We can go to a game to see <u>a team</u> play.

   _____

5. We can watch <u>a movie</u> in a big theater.

   _____

6. We can go shopping at <u>a store</u> to get new shoes.

   _____

A common noun names any person, place, or thing. A proper noun names a specific person, place, or thing. A proper noun begins with a capital letter.

Proper Noun	Common Noun
Doctor Moore	doctor
Ms. Kelly	woman
Duke	dog
Third Street	street
South Street School	school
Florida	state
Africa	continent

Underline the proper nouns. Capitalize the first letter.

1. We are going to florida with relatives.

2. We will drive because mom does not like airplanes.

3. We are staying at the sunny days motel.

4. The brochure says the motel is near the atlantic ocean.

5. I hope we can also drive to see disney world.

6. My aunt emma says we should tour a city like miami.

7. I really want to visit reptile world and see alligators and crocodiles.

8. I have to buy a picture of an alligator called giant gus for my friend!

Bonus: Go back and circle the common nouns in the sentences. There are a total of ten.

Fill in the bubble next to the correct answer.

1. Which sentence has a singular possessive noun?

Ⓐ The flower has petals and leaves.

Ⓑ Those flowers' leaves are fuzzy.

Ⓒ The flowers petals are smooth.

Ⓓ The flower's petals are yellow.

2. Which sentence has two plural possessive nouns?

Ⓐ The fans' shouts were louder than the players' cheers.

Ⓑ The teams' scores were closer than the coach's guess.

Ⓒ The game's closing minutes were the most exciting.

Ⓓ The winners shook hands with the losers.

3. Which sentence has the correct possessive of *cat*?

Ⓐ A cats claws are sharp.

Ⓑ A cat's whiskers are sensitive.

Ⓒ A cats' fur sheds in warm weather.

Ⓓ The paws of the cat are soft.

4. Which sentence has only proper nouns?

Ⓐ San Francisco has the Golden Gate Bridge.

Ⓑ New York has the Brooklyn Bridge and a famous statue.

Ⓒ San Antonio has a famous fort known as the Alamo.

Ⓓ Washington, D.C., has many memorials.

5. Complete the sentence with the noun that gives the most information.
   _____ *is having a special party with a space theme tonight.*

Ⓐ museum

Ⓑ astronaut

Ⓒ restaurant

Ⓓ Fifth Planet Diner

Name _____

Adjectives can tell what kind, how many, and which one.

What Kind	**tall** trees	**popular** students	**long** letter
How Many	**ten** trees	**several** students	**one** letter
Which One	**those** trees	**these** students	**this** letter

Read the sentence and the type of adjective you will need to complete it.
Then circle the correct adjective.

1. There are _____ students going on the boat trip. (how many)
          (excited, twelve, these)

2. We have to find _____ students and take a photograph of them. (which one)
          (ten, tall, those)

3. The trip will make a _____ story in our school newspaper. (what kind)
          (second, thrilling, this)

4. It is not often that _____ students from the same school win a trip. (how many)
          (several, excellent, these)

5. They expect to see _____ whales where they are headed. (what kind)
          (those, gigantic, some)

6. Every student in school will enter _____ contest next year! (which one)
          (that, one, writing)

7. Everyone wants to win an _____ trip. (what kind)
          (one, exciting, that)

8. Kylie has already chosen her _____ topic! (which one)
          (two, amazing, next)

An adjective is a word that describes a noun or a pronoun.

The **white** car is **clean**.

White is an adjective that describes *car.* It comes before the noun.

Clean is also an adjective that describes *car.* It is called a predicate adjective because it follows the verb *is* in the sentence.

Underline each adjective in the sentences.
Write the letters *PA* above each predicate adjective.

1. The sky looks dark.

2. A fierce storm is coming.

3. There will be heavy rain that could turn into icy sleet.

4. High winds are often dangerous.

5. Let's put the outdoor furniture inside the empty shed.

6. Our dog is afraid of the thunder and lightning!

7. The old fellow is miserable in a storm.

8. But give him a big hug and he is happy.

9. Our calico cat is in the bedroom closet.

10. She will experience the raging storm curled up on soft blankets!

     Language Fundamentals • EMC 2754 • © Evan-Moor Corp.

Adjectives can be words that describe how a noun looks, feels, sounds, smells, or tastes.

How It Looks	**pink** sunset
How It Feels	**scratchy** sweater
How It Sounds	**whistling** wind
How It Smells	**stinky** dog
How It Tastes	**salty** snack

Write an adjective from the box to describe each noun. On the line below each sentence, explain if the adjective describes how the noun looks, feels, sounds, smells, or tastes.

vanilla   red   delicious   country   noisy   warm

1. The _____ restaurant is filled with people talking.

_____

2. The dining room is _____ from the huge fireplace.

_____

3. The tables are set with _____ dishes.

_____

4. The _____ candles make the room smell nice.

_____

5. The waiters play _____ music on fiddles.

_____

6. The cook makes _____ food.

_____

Fill in the bubble next to the correct answer.

1. Find the adjective that describes how something feels.
   The children are asleep under the two soft blankets.

   Ⓐ asleep

   Ⓑ under

   Ⓒ two

   Ⓓ soft

2. Which sentence has a predicate adjective?

   Ⓐ The loud noise is coming from the yard.

   Ⓑ The dog is hungry and wants to be fed.

   Ⓒ His crunchy treats are in the pantry.

   Ⓓ He will eat them all at once!

3. Complete the sentence with the adjective that tells what kind.
   The _____ explorer headed into the dark cave.

   Ⓐ daring

   Ⓑ other

   Ⓒ one

   Ⓓ last

4. Complete the sentence with the adjective that tells which one.
   _____ houses are perfect for big families.

   Ⓐ Roomy

   Ⓑ These

   Ⓒ Second

   Ⓓ Big

5. Complete the sentence with the adjective that tells how many.
   The apples had _____ seeds.

   Ⓐ those

   Ⓑ large

   Ⓒ few

   Ⓓ tiny

Name _____

Adjectives can be used to make comparisons.

- Add *-er* to an adjective to compare two people, places, or things. Adjectives with *-er* are called comparative adjectives.

  The Grand Canyon is **deeper** than Glen Canyon.

- Add *-est* to an adjective to compare three or more people, places, or things. Adjectives with *-est* are called superlative adjectives.

  The canyon is the **deepest** I have seen.

Read each sentence. Circle the correct form of the adjective to complete the sentence.

1. The _____ part of the Atlantic is the Puerto Rico Trench.   deeper   deepest

2. The Atlantic Ocean is the second _____ of the oceans.   younger   youngest

3. The _____ part of both oceans is near the equator.   warmer   warmest

4. The leatherback turtle dives _____ than penguins.   deeper   deepest

5. Many people think dolphins are the _____ ocean animals.   smarter   smartest

6. The swordfish swims _____ than sharks.   faster   fastest

7. The sea horse is _____ than the eel.   slower   slowest

8. The blue whale is the _____ animal in the ocean.   louder   loudest

9. The gray whale has the _____ migration of all the whales.   longer   longest

10. The ice in Antarctica is _____ than the ice in the Arctic.   thicker   thickest

> Comparative adjectives use *–er* to compare two people, places, or things.
>
> A village is small**er** than a city.
>
> Superlative adjectives use *–est* to compare three or more people, places, or things.
>
> They are the rich**est** family in town.

Add *–er* or *–est* to the correct adjective from the word box to complete each sentence.

fast	high	clean	long	deep
hard	near	warm	tall	soon

1. We are taking our _____ vacation this year.

2. We are staying at the hotel _____ to the shore.

3. It is _____ to get to the beach from here than from farther away.

4. It is _____ in the pool than in the ocean.

5. This is the _____ beach I have ever seen.

6. I worked all day to make the _____ sand castle on the beach.

7. Molding the sand was _____ than I thought.

8. I dug _____ than before to get wet sand.

9. The waves are _____ than they were yesterday.

10. We got to the beach _____ today.

> Some adjectives have irregular comparative and superlative forms.
>
> That was a **good** book.
> This was a **better** book.
> I read the **best** book.
>
> Other adjectives with irregular forms for making comparisons:
>
> | bad | many | little |
> |------|------|--------|
> | worse | more | less |
> | worst | most | least |

Change each underlined word to the correct form of the adjective.
Write it on the line.

1. That was the <u>bad</u> concert I have ever heard! _____

2. There were <u>many</u> mistakes than the last time. _____

3. The <u>better</u> sound came from the saxophones. _____

4. The tuba players were <u>worst</u> than the drummers. _____

5. The <u>less</u> mistakes were made by the cymbalists. _____

6. Those band members did a <u>best</u> job overall. _____

7. The trumpets were the <u>more</u> out of tune. _____

8. I think they got <u>little</u> practice than the other instruments. _____

9. I know I am the <u>worse</u> critic of our band. _____

10. Still, I know the band can be <u>good</u> than that! _____

Fill in the bubble next to the correct answer.

1. Complete the sentence with the correct form of the adjective.
   Those clouds are the _____ in the sky.
   Ⓐ dark
   Ⓑ darker
   Ⓒ darkest
   Ⓓ darkening

2. Which sentence is correct?
   Ⓐ I ordered the worst sandwich on the menu.
   Ⓑ She has the better pie of all.
   Ⓒ His food was best than mine.
   Ⓓ Our food was worser than his.

3. Which adjective would be used to compare two stars?
   Ⓐ bright
   Ⓑ brighter
   Ⓒ brightest
   Ⓓ brighten

4. Which sentence is correct?
   Ⓐ Whales are the largest mammals.
   Ⓑ Whales are the larger of all mammals.
   Ⓒ Whales are largest than fish.
   Ⓓ Whales are large than sharks.

5. How many adjectives are in this sentence?
   We will have less money but more time if we take this train.
   Ⓐ one
   Ⓑ two
   Ⓒ three
   Ⓓ four

> Proper adjectives are made from some proper nouns that name specific places. Proper adjectives have different endings and spellings.
> All proper adjectives begin with a capital letter.
>
> I live in **America,** and my friend lives in **England.**
>
> He calls me his **American** buddy, and I call him my **English** pal.

Underline the proper adjective and circle the proper noun that make a pair.
The first one has been done for you.

1. In Egypt, we saw statues of Egyptian kings and learned about English explorers.

2. We enjoyed French food in France and in parts of Africa.

3. People who moved from Europe to Africa brought European customs with them.

4. We heard many African and European languages all through Africa.

5. We took an Italian boat from Egypt and landed in Italy.

6. We weren't in Belgium, but we still had Belgian waffles in Italy.

7. We went to Switzerland to see the Swiss villages and then flew to Sweden.

8. We didn't eat any Swedish meatballs in Sweden, but we did have Swiss cheese.

9. From Sweden, we went to Norway and had Norwegian chocolate.

10. Everywhere in Europe there were Chinese restaurants, as though we were in China!

Some proper adjectives are made from proper nouns that name specific places.

- Proper adjectives begin with a capital letter. Many proper adjectives end in *–ese*, *–ian*, *–ish*, or *–ean*.

ese	ian	ish	ean
Chin**ese**	Egypt**ian**	Ir**ish**	Chil**ean**
Portugu**ese**	Brazil**ian**	Span**ish**	Europ**ean**
Vietnam**ese**	Russ**ian**	Swed**ish**	Kor**ean**

- Others have spellings different from the proper noun.

French   Greek   Swiss

Complete each sentence with the proper adjective made from the proper noun given.

1. The _____ Union is made up of 25 member countries.
   (Europe)

2. The _____ Resistance during World War II was famous.
   (France)

3. _____ mythology is filled with adventure.
   (Greece)

4. The _____ New Year is celebrated for fifteen days.
   (China)

5. The samba is a _____ dance.
   (Brazil)

6. _____ explorers charted much of the Americas.
   (Spain)

7. The _____ pyramids are one of the Seven Wonders of the World.
   (Egypt)

8. _____ chalets are located high in the Alps.
   (Switzerland)

Fill in the bubble next to the correct answer.

1. Which underlined word is a proper adjective?

   Ⓐ <u>Paris</u> has lots of great museums.

   Ⓑ I met a <u>Parisian</u> woman on the train.

   Ⓒ We did not have time to see <u>Italy</u>.

   Ⓓ I will visit <u>Rome</u> on the next trip.

2. Which proper noun belongs with the underlined proper adjective?
   The <u>Iraqi</u> civilization is very old.

   Ⓐ Iran

   Ⓑ Iraq

   Ⓒ India

   Ⓓ Ireland

3. Which sentence correctly names a proper adjective?

   Ⓐ Many students in our class have Russian relatives.

   Ⓑ One student has grandparents who are Rushish.

   Ⓒ There are several students who come from Russia.

   Ⓓ They speak the language of Russia.

4. Which sentence correctly names the proper noun and proper adjective?

   Ⓐ We ate some Chilean food.

   Ⓑ Chile is a beautiful country!

   Ⓒ We had to get some Chilese dollars before we left for Chile.

   Ⓓ We saw fascinating Chilean cities on our travels in Chile.

5. Which word is <u>not</u> the correct proper adjective for a country?

   Ⓐ Portuguese

   Ⓑ Vietnamian

   Ⓒ Irish

   Ⓓ French

Name _____

A pronoun is a word used in place of a noun.

I   he   she   it   they   we   me   you   him   her   them   us

Jacob has the games. **Emily and Olivia** have the food.
He has the games. **They** have the food.

Sonjay will meet **Ethan and Ryan. Aki** will come with **Madison and me.**
Sonjay will meet **them. She** will come with **us.**

Replace the underlined nouns with the correct pronouns.

1. <u>Daniel and I</u> are taking a train trip.

   _____ are taking a train trip.

2. I have traveled alone, but <u>Daniel</u> has not.

   I have traveled alone, but _____ has not.

3. <u>Mom and Dad</u> are working and cannot visit <u>our grandparents</u>.

   _____ are working and cannot visit _____.

4. <u>Mom</u> says <u>the train</u> is the best way to go.

   _____ says _____ is the best way to go.

5. I'm bringing games and snacks for <u>Daniel and me</u>.

   I'm bringing games and snacks for _____.

6. I am glad to be going with <u>Daniel</u>.

   I am glad to be going with _____.

Language Fundamentals • EMC 2754 • © Evan-Moor Corp.

A pronoun is used in place of a noun.

I   me   you   he   she   him   her   it   they   them   we   us

- Use pronouns to avoid repeating the same names in a sentence.

  Joshua is meeting Caleb and David, and **Joshua** is late.

  Joshua is meeting Caleb and David, and **he** is late.

- Use pronouns to avoid repeating the same words in a group of sentences.

  The shells I found on the beach are in my suitcase. **The shells** are pink and white. **The shells** will go in my collection.

  The shells I found on the beach are in my suitcase. **They** are pink and white. **They** will go in my collection.

Read the paragraphs. Replace the underlined words with the correct pronouns. Write the pronouns above the words.

Ashley is getting a new bike. The bike is the first new bike for Ashley in four years. Mom pretended not to listen to Ashley when Ashley asked for a new bike. Mom knew that a bike would make a great birthday present.

Mom and I went to pick out the bike. Mom and I looked at all of the bikes. Mr. Brown, the store manager, told Mom and me that orange is a popular color. Mom and I decided that Ashley would like an orange bike. Mom paid Mr. Brown for the orange bike. Mr. Brown carried the orange bike to the car. Now all Mom and I have to do is wait for Ashley's birthday. Ashley will be surprised!

> A singular pronoun takes the place of one person, place, or thing.
>
> I   you   he   she   it   me   him   her
>
> **The tornado** is dangerous.   The tornado surprised **the weatherman**.
>
> **It** is dangerous.   The tornado surprised **him**.

Replace each underlined noun with the correct singular pronoun.

1. <u>Mrs. Ray</u> heard the storm warning on the radio.

   _____ heard the storm warning on the radio.

2. Mrs. Ray called <u>Selena</u> for help.

   Mrs. Ray called _____ for help.

3. <u>Selena</u> brought <u>Jared</u> to have an extra pair of hands.

   _____ brought _____ to have an extra pair of hands.

4. <u>Jared</u> told <u>Mrs. Ray</u> to go down to the basement.

   _____ told _____ to go down to the basement.

5. <u>The dog</u> is the main thing <u>Mrs. Ray</u> is worried about.

   _____ is the main thing _____ is worried about.

6. When <u>Jared</u> brought <u>the dog</u> to the basement, <u>Mrs. Ray</u> gave <u>Jared</u> a big hug!

   When _____ brought _____ to the basement,

   _____ gave _____ a big hug!

Name _____

> A plural pronoun takes the place of more than one person, place, or thing.
>
> they   we   them   us   you
>
> The umpire is looking for **the coaches.**   **The umpire and I** are ready to start.
>
> The umpire is looking for **them.**   **We** are ready to start.

Rewrite each sentence with the correct plural pronoun for the underlined nouns.

1. <u>The players</u> have a problem today.

   _____

2. The field is wet, and <u>the teams</u> don't want to play.

   _____

3. <u>The coaches and I</u> agree with the players.

   _____

4. It can be dangerous for <u>the fielders</u> to run on wet grass.

   _____

5. The best plan for <u>the teams</u> is to wait for the field to dry.

   _____

6. The umpire has an idea for <u>you and me</u>.

   _____

Fill in the bubble next to the correct answer.

1. Which sentence tells what pronouns do?

   Ⓐ Pronouns take the place of verbs in a sentence.

   Ⓑ Pronouns take the place of any noun in a sentence.

   Ⓒ Pronouns take the place of too many words in a sentence.

   Ⓓ Pronouns take the place of adjectives in a sentence.

2. Which sentence contains a pronoun?

   Ⓐ Riley brought a large bouquet to share.

   Ⓑ Dylan brought ten roses for the teachers.

   Ⓒ Christina brought flower baskets for the teachers.

   Ⓓ Grace brought them flowers to wear.

3. Choose the best way to avoid repeating names in this sentence.
   Lily and Nicholas like the same book, and Lily and Nicholas want to share the book.

   Ⓐ Lily and Nicholas like the same book, and they want to share it.

   Ⓑ Lily and he like the same book, and Lily and he want to share it.

   Ⓒ Lily and Nicholas like the same book, and she and Nicholas want to share it.

   Ⓓ She and he like the same book, and they want to share it.

4. Which sentence has two singular pronouns?

   Ⓐ You need help with those math problems.

   Ⓑ I need help with a problem in math class.

   Ⓒ You are a good student, and I need help with math.

   Ⓓ I can't figure out the answer to these problems.

5. Which sentence has two plural pronouns?

   Ⓐ The cat is hungry, and we can't find the food.

   Ⓑ The cat will bug us until we feed him.

   Ⓒ They gave him food, and he is still hungry!

   Ⓓ He will cry until we feed him again!

 Language Fundamentals • EMC 2754 • © Evan-Moor Corp.

A subject pronoun replaces a noun that is the subject of a sentence. It tells who or what the sentence is about.

I   you   he   she   it   we   they

The girls are taking a trip. **Lydia** is going, too.

They are taking a trip. **She** is going, too.

Read the words in parentheses ( ). Write the correct subject pronoun in each sentence.

1. _____ are in Washington, D.C.
    (Nathan and Julia)

2. _____ is visiting the city with his family.
    (Nathan)

3. _____ went with her Girl Scout troop.
    (Julia)

4. _____ would like to be there, too.
    (You and I)

5. _____ is an exciting city with many beautiful monuments.
    (Washington, D.C.)

6. _____ are named after important presidents like Lincoln and Jefferson.
    (The monuments)

7. _____ want to go to the top of the Washington Monument!
    (My friends and I)

8. _____ can decide what you want to see in our nation's capital.
    (You and your friends)

Name _____

> An object pronoun follows an action verb or words such as *about, at, for, of, to,* and *with.*
>
> me   you   him   her   it   us   them
>
> The chorus will sing for **us.** They have songbooks with **them.**
>
> The band is too loud for **me.** The conductor is looking at **you** to start.

Circle the object pronouns in the sentences.

1. The school band or chorus would be fun for us to join.

2. Singing in the chorus would be great for you to try.

3. You know all the groups and sing along with them constantly.

4. I know the chorus practices after school. I've heard it many times.

5. I don't have a good voice, so playing an instrument is better for me.

6. Mr. Jimenez said I can talk with him about learning the trumpet.

7. My sister says if I play the trumpet at home, I will drive her crazy.

8. I know I can learn it, and she might even enjoy it!

9. Our friends will hear us perform at school concerts.

10. Sophia will come if we ask her in time.

11. Nina and Carlos will sit in the front row where we can see them.

12. Isaac will be in the back, but we'll still hear him cheer.

> A possessive pronoun shows ownership. Some possessive pronouns are used before a noun.
>
> **her   his   its   my   our   their   your**
>
> Lian is **my** friend.
> Mr. Chan is **our** neighbor.
> That is **their** house.

Underline the possessive pronouns. Circle the noun that comes after each one.

1. A new building is going up in our neighborhood.

2. Dad heard at his gym that it will be a huge store.

3. The store has a sign with its grand opening date.

4. The construction workers start their day very early.

5. You can hear them working all through our house.

6. My brother complains that the noise is loudest in his room.

7. I tell him to turn up his stereo.

8. My sister wears her earmuffs around the house.

9. My dad wears his earplugs from work.

10. I just go to stay with my friend.

11. Mom says her solution is to think about the store and its advantages.

12. Our family will save time in traveling, and my parents will save on gas for their cars.

A possessive pronoun shows ownership. Some possessive pronouns stand alone.

mine   his   hers   ours   yours   theirs

This guidebook is **mine.**

Sabrena and Earl say the map is **theirs.**

Do you have **yours?**

Write the correct possessive pronoun for the underlined noun.

1. Do <u>you</u> know which suitcase is _____?

2. <u>My</u> bag is purple, but I don't see _____.

3. <u>Trisha</u> says _____ is missing.

4. <u>We</u> think it's a bad way for this trip of _____ to start!

5. There is <u>Percy's</u> suitcase, so he has _____.

6. <u>Ramon</u> is relieved to get _____, too.

7. We're missing our things, but at least <u>they</u> have _____.

8. We can borrow clean clothes from them until <u>we</u> get _____.

9. <u>Myrtle</u> and I are the same size, so I can wear _____.

10. Who knows when <u>I</u> will get _____!

> When a pronoun takes the place of a noun, it must agree with the noun it is replacing.
>
> • Singular pronouns replace singular nouns.
>
> > **Mina** is going to **her** dance class. Then **she** can go to the library.
>
> • Plural pronouns replace plural nouns.
>
> > The dance teacher is proud of her **students**. **They** are ready for **their** recital.

In each pair of sentences, circle the pronouns and underline the nouns that they replace. Write *singular* or *plural* on the line.

1. The dance contest is tomorrow. It will be very exciting to watch. _____

2. Students are putting on the show. They have done a lot of work. _____

3. Ms. Kumar is the dance teacher. Her class will start the contest. _____

4. A teacher from another dance school is here. He is the judge. _____

5. Most dancers have the music with them. _____

6. Two girls are dancing to ballet music. It sounds beautiful. _____

7. Three students dance to hip-hop music. Their moves are amazing! _____

8. One boy puts on his tap shoes and music. He is the best so far. _____

9. Takara is nervous during her turn, and she trips on stage. _____

10. Each dancer gets applause from friends. They want their favorite to win. _____

> When a pronoun takes the place of a noun, it must agree with the noun it is replacing in gender and number.

Incorrect	Correct
Luke brought a spotted **frog** to school.	**Luke** brought a spotted **frog** to school.
She brought **them** to school.	**He** brought **it** to school.

Read each pair of sentences. Write *correct* if the pronouns in sentence *b* agree with the underlined nouns in sentence *a*. If the pronouns do not agree with the nouns, rewrite the second sentence.

1. *a.* <u>Zachary</u> is working on a <u>project</u> for the school science fair.

   b. He is doing it on weather.

   _____

2. *a.* <u>Ella</u> is collecting different kinds of <u>flowers</u> for her project.

   b. They put it in vases all over the house.

   _____

3. *a.* <u>Mia and some other students</u> are making a huge <u>dinosaur</u> from cardboard.

   b. She will display it in the hallway.

   _____

4. *a.* <u>Jose and Tony</u> took <u>photographs</u> of clouds.

   b. He made it into a slideshow on the computer.

   _____

Fill in the bubble next to the correct answer.

1. Which sentence has a subject pronoun?

   Ⓐ Our house is full of relatives.

   Ⓑ The bad weather is forcing us to stay inside.

   Ⓒ Much fun will be had by everyone.

   Ⓓ They have come to spend the holiday.

2. Which sentence has an object pronoun?

   Ⓐ Haley says there is a comet named for her.

   Ⓑ I have read about Haley's comet in science.

   Ⓒ It comes by Earth every 76 years.

   Ⓓ It is way too old to be named for a fourth-grader!

3. How many possessive pronouns are in this sentence?
   Their report was longer than ours.

   Ⓐ one

   Ⓑ two

   Ⓒ three

   Ⓓ four

4. Which word does the pronoun *his* replace?
   Jacob can't play soccer. He is watching his baby sister.

   Ⓐ Jacob

   Ⓑ play

   Ⓒ soccer

   Ⓓ sister

5. Choose the sentence that shows the correct agreement.
   Brianna is one of the fastest runners in the race.

   Ⓐ She can win them.

   Ⓑ They can win it.

   Ⓒ She can win it.

   Ⓓ They can win her.

A verb is a word that shows action or state of being.
The verb is the main word in the predicate.

Predicate

Eric **draws** pictures for a comic book.

Verb

Predicate

Our art teacher **is** happy with their work.

Verb

Underline the verb in each sentence.

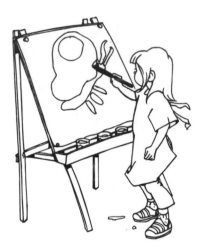

1. The students work with watercolors today.

2. Susan dips her brush in water.

3. She is careful with her paint.

4. Painters slide their brushes across the paper.

5. Susan spilled her water!

Choose a verb from the word box to complete each sentence.

chooses   took   lift   gives   wave

6. The art students _____ their paints outside.

7. Mr. Lee _____ a new brush to Eric.

8. Eric slowly _____ a beautiful green paint.

9. The trees _____ in the breeze.

10. The artists _____ their brushes.

> An action verb tells what the subject is doing. Most action verbs name actions that we can easily see or hear.
>
> My dad **loaded** the dishwasher.
>
> Mom **shouts** from the kitchen.

Draw a line from each subject to its action verb. Then read each sentence.

1. Dancers   •   • roasts.

2. The carpenter •   • hammers.

3. Gardeners   •   • leap.

4. The chef   •   • plant.

Fill in each blank with an action verb.

5. Noah _____ his bike to Nathan's house.

6. The boys _____ a tall tree.

7. Birds _____ from the branches.

8. Squirrels _____ acorns.

Write two sentences, each with an action verb.

9. _____

_____

10. _____

_____

> An action verb tells what the subject is doing. Some action verbs name actions that we cannot see or hear.
>
> Tanya **thinks** about her old friends.
>
> She **misses** them.

Circle the verb that names an action that cannot be seen or heard.
Write it on the line.

1. Tanya wishes for an e-mail message from Amy. _____

2. Amy always forgets! _____

3. She prefers a phone call. _____

4. Amy finally remembers. _____

5. Both girls like music. _____

6. Tanya dreams of a career as a singer. _____

7. She loves to sing. _____

8. Amy cares more about science. _____

9. She wonders about other planets. _____

10. Both girls imagine a bright future. _____

11. Sometimes they worry. _____

12. Still, they hope their dreams come true! _____

A linking verb can link the subject to a noun that names the subject. Linking verbs include forms of the verb *to be.*

am   was   are   were   be   will   is

Subject	Linking Verb	Noun
The Pilgrims	were	early settlers.

A linking verb can link the subject to an adjective that describes the subject.

Subject	Linking Verb	Adjective
The winters	are	cold in Massachusetts.

Choose a subject from Box A and a noun or an adjective from Box B. Link them with a form of the verb *to be.* Write the sentences on the lines.

Box A	
• History	• We
• The Pilgrims	• I
• Freedom	

Box B	
• students	• interesting
• brave	• their
• an American	• goal

1. _____

2. _____

3. _____

4. _____

5. _____

Name _____

A linking verb links the subject to a noun or an adjective that names or describes it. In addition to *to be*, other linking verbs include:

appear	become	feel	grow	look
remain	seem	smell	sound	taste

Joe **seems** fascinated by that book.

The cover **looks** interesting.

Circle the linking verb in each sentence.

1. The library seems busy today.

2. That librarian looks annoyed.

3. After an hour of searching for just the right book, I grew tired.

4. I remained determined to find it, however.

Underline the verb in each sentence. Then circle the correct words to tell whether it is an action verb or a linking verb.

5. The explorers in the book sailed the seas.   Action Verb   Linking Verb

6. Captain Fife was my favorite character.   Action Verb   Linking Verb

7. In this picture, he looks brave.   Action Verb   Linking Verb

8. Maybe I will be an explorer someday!   Action Verb   Linking Verb

Write two sentences, each with a linking verb from the rule box.

9. _____

_____

10. _____

_____

Language Fundamentals • EMC 2754 • © Evan-Moor Corp.

Fill in the bubble next to the correct answer.

1. Which of these is the correct definition of a verb?

   Ⓐ A verb is a word that names a person, place, or thing.

   Ⓑ A verb is a word that describes a noun.

   Ⓒ A verb is a word that shows an action or a state of being.

   Ⓓ A verb is a word that takes the place of a noun.

2. Which sentence contains an action verb?

   Ⓐ Ms. Conroy delivers the mail.

   Ⓑ Bobby is hungry.

   Ⓒ That dog seems friendly.

   Ⓓ The flowers smell fresh.

3. Which sentence has a verb naming an action that we can't see?

   Ⓐ I thought about you today.

   Ⓑ My friend ran to meet me.

   Ⓒ Kim calls her best friend every night.

   Ⓓ Lindsey jumped up and ran to the door.

4. Which sentence contains a linking verb?

   Ⓐ I walk home every day.

   Ⓑ My house is only one block from here.

   Ⓒ My dog greets me with a wag of her tail.

   Ⓓ Mom makes a snack for me.

5. Which sentence contains a linking verb?

   Ⓐ I put on boots this morning.

   Ⓑ I brought an umbrella.

   Ⓒ It looks like rain today.

   Ⓓ The clouds hang heavy in the sky.

Name _____

> Verbs have special forms called tenses that tell when the action takes place.
>
> **Present Tense**   My mom **plays** golf.
> (is happening now)
>
> **Past Tense**   She **played** last weekend.
> (has already happened)
>
> **Future Tense**   She **will play** next Saturday, too.
> (is going to happen)

Underline the verb in each sentence. Circle the word that names the correct verb tense.

1. Susan and Nancy play golf.	Present	Past	Future
2. Last Saturday, they went to the course.	Present	Past	Future
3. Rain fell on the golfers.	Present	Past	Future
4. They carried big umbrellas.	Present	Past	Future
5. Today, Nancy has new clubs.	Present	Past	Future
6. They were a present for her birthday.	Present	Past	Future
7. She hits the ball hard.	Present	Past	Future
8. Susan will ride in the golf cart.	Present	Past	Future
9. Nancy watches the ball fly.	Present	Past	Future
10. The ball will land right in the hole!	Present	Past	Future
11. Nancy got a hole in one!	Present	Past	Future
12. She will receive a trophy.	Present	Past	Future

Language Fundamentals • EMC 2754 • © Evan-Moor Corp.

A present tense verb shows that something is happening now or happens regularly.

Is Happening Now   I **see** a snail in the garden!
Happens Regularly   Tulips **bloom** every spring.

Underline the sentence in each pair that is in the present tense.

1. Shirley plants seeds in the rich soil. The seeds will sprout quickly.

2. Michael dug a deep hole for a new tree. Now he is watering it.

3. Young trees need lots of water. This tree will grow tall.

4. Shirley and Michael tend their garden. It will be full of flowers soon.

5. They will pick flowers for their mother. She loves flowers.

6. The sun shines on the garden. They will wait until spring.

Fill in each blank with a present tense verb from the word box below.
Then read each sentence. Circle the word that tells whether the action
is happening now or happens regularly.

eat   destroy   leaves   see

7. I _____ a snail on the leaf.   now   regularly

8. Snails _____ at night.   now   regularly

9. Sometimes they _____ the plants.   now   regularly

10. That snail _____ a slimy trail behind.   now   regularly

> Both action verbs and linking verbs can be in the present tense.
>
> **Present Tense Action Verb**   The police officer **directs** traffic.
>
> **Present Tense Linking Verb**   That car **looks** amazing!

Underline the present tense verb in each sentence. Decide whether the verb is an action verb or a linking verb. Write *action* or *linking* on the line.

1. Jordan's dad sells cars.   _____

2. Jordan seems very interested in cars and trucks.   _____

3. Jordan and his dad name all the different kinds of cars.   _____

4. They are experts on cars!   _____

5. Jordan and his dad wash that convertible every Saturday.   _____

Choose a present tense verb from the word box to complete each sentence.

> zooms   drive   bounces   looks   repair

6. Traffic _____ along the highway.

7. Mechanics _____ cars at that gas station.

8. Our truck _____ dirty today.

9. Aunt Rachel and Uncle Henry _____ a jeep in the country.

10. The SUV _____ along dirt roads.

A past tense verb tells about something that happened in the past and is over.

My family **traveled** to France last year.

My grandfather once **studied** in Paris.

He **was** an art student.

Underline the sentence that tells about something that has happened or was in the past. Circle the past tense verb.

1. Paris is the capital city of France. My grandfather lived there for a year.

2. My grandfather works in advertising. In Paris, he took art classes.

3. My family went to France on vacation. I remember everything about our trip.

4. I have a photo album full of pictures. I took a dozen pictures of the Eiffel Tower.

5. Gustave Eiffel designed the tower in the year 1889. It is tall and beautiful.

Write three sentences about a place that you have visited. Use a past tense verb in each sentence.

6. _____

_____

7. _____

_____

8. _____

_____

> The past tense of most verbs is formed by adding *ed.* The verbs that follow this rule are called regular verbs.
>
> **Present Tense**   We **play** basketball on Saturdays.
> **Past Tense**   We **played** for an hour last week.

Write the past tense of these regular verbs.

1. walk   _____

5. laugh   _____

2. wash   _____

6. call   _____

3. cook   _____

7. tramp   _____

4. open   _____

8. turn   _____

Write each sentence in the past tense.

9. The players pass the ball back and forth.

_____

10. The fans shout from the stands.

_____

11. I return the ball to the referee.

_____

12. The fans roar with excitement!

_____

Some regular verbs require spelling changes before adding *ed* to form the past tense.

- When a verb ends in a silent *e*, drop the silent *e* and add *ed*.

  move ⟶ mov**ed**   wave ⟶ wav**ed**   hope ⟶ hop**ed**

- When a verb ends in a consonant followed by a *y*, change the *y* to *i* and add *ed*.

  cry ⟶ cr**ied**   study ⟶ stud**ied**   hurry ⟶ hurr**ied**

- When a verb ends in a short vowel followed by a single consonant, double the final consonant and add *ed*.

  hop ⟶ hop**ped**   grab ⟶ grab**bed**   trim ⟶ trim**med**

Complete each sentence with the past tense form of the verb in parentheses ( ).

1. Riley _____ his cat Domino.
   (name)

2. Domino _____ to catch a mouse in the kitchen.
   (try)

3. Riley _____ the mouse, too.
   (chase)

4. The mouse _____ a crust of bread as it ran.
   (carry)

5. Riley _____ on his shoelace.
   (trip)

6. Domino's whiskers _____ .
   (wiggle)

7. Riley _____ the mouse behind the cookie jar.
   (spy)

8. The little mouse _____ a cookie crumb.
   (drop)

> Some verbs do not follow a set rule to form the past tense. These verbs are called irregular verbs.
>
> **Present** We **buy** groceries every week.   I **eat** breakfast in the kitchen.
>
> **Past** We **bought** maple syrup for our pancakes.   Yesterday, I **ate** a bowl of cereal.

Complete each sentence with the correct past tense verb in parentheses ( ).

1. I _____ late on Saturday.
   (sleeped, slept)

2. My alarm clock _____ at 7 o'clock.
   (rang, ringed)

3. I _____ off the annoying sound.
   (shut, shutted)

4. I _____ asleep again.
   (falled, fell)

5. At 9 o'clock in the morning, I _____.
   (rose, rised)

6. At last, I _____ my feet to the floor.
   (swung, swinged)

7. My feet _____ on the cold floor.
   (freezed, froze)

8. I _____ under the covers again!
   (hid, hided)

Name _____

Verbs that do not follow a set rule to form the past tense are called irregular verbs. Many verbs that we use every day have an irregular past tense.

Present I **go** to the skating rink every week.   I always **buy** a snack there.

Past I **went** just last Thursday.   Last time, I **bought** an ice-cream bar.

Write the past tense form of each irregular verb.

Present	Irregular Past	Present	Irregular Past
1. ride	_____	9. fly	_____
2. come	_____	10. begin	_____
3. give	_____	11. see	_____
4. do	_____	12. pay	_____
5. have	_____	13. teach	_____
6. is	_____	14. wear	_____
7. win	_____	15. find	_____
8. bring	_____	16. throw	_____

Write four sentences, each with an irregular past tense verb.

17. _____

18. _____

19. _____

20. _____

Fill in the bubble next to the correct answer.

1. What does the verb tense tell us?

   Ⓐ The verb tense tells when the action takes place.

   Ⓑ The verb tense tells where the action takes place.

   Ⓒ The verb tense tells who is performing the action.

   Ⓓ The verb tense tells us what the action is about.

2. Which sentence is in the present tense?

   Ⓐ Willie turned on the lights.

   Ⓑ Sam sat in his desk.

   Ⓒ Paula talks to the teacher.

   Ⓓ Kayla was late today.

3. What does the past tense of a verb show?

   Ⓐ The past tense shows that the action is taking place now.

   Ⓑ The past tense shows that the action took place before now and is over.

   Ⓒ The past tense shows that the action has not yet taken place.

   Ⓓ The past tense shows that the action might take place.

4. Which of these is the past tense of the verb *tap?*

   Ⓐ taped

   Ⓑ tapt

   Ⓒ tappet

   Ⓓ tapped

5. Which of these is the past tense of the verb *cry?*

   Ⓐ cryed

   Ⓑ cride

   Ⓒ criied

   Ⓓ cried

> Helping verbs come before the main verb. They help the main verb show time or tell more about the action.
>
> | | | | | | | |
> |---|---|---|---|---|---|---|
> | am | was | being | does | has | might | should |
> | are | were | been | did | had | can | would |
> | is | be | do | have | may | could | will |
>
> Mr. Richards **has** chosen the actors for the play.
>
> I **had** hoped to get a part.
>
> I **am** helping with the sets and costumes instead.

Circle the helping verb and underline the main verb in each sentence.

1. The play was written by a famous author.

2. I am reading the first act now.

3. Leslie has walked onto the stage.

4. She was given the biggest part in the play.

5. Bob might build the sets with me.

Fill in each blank with the correct helping verb from the word box below. Then read the sentences.

> is   might   has   are   am

6. Bob and I _____ pounding nails into the set.

7. I _____ working hard.

8. Leslie _____ practicing her first speech.

9. Mr. Richards _____ told her to speak louder.

10. The play _____ be a big hit!

A helping verb helps the main verb state the action or show time. In questions, the subject comes between the helping verb and the main verb.

Are you **going** on the field trip?

Will the blacksmith **make** a horseshoe?

Has the bus **arrived** yet?

Circle the subject. Underline the helping verb and the main verb in each question.

1. Is the bus taking us to the historic village today?

2. Will Ms. Kampo tell us about life in the olden days?

3. Can you see the blacksmith?

4. Is he hammering a horseshoe?

Unscramble each set of words to form a question and write it on the line. Circle the helping verb.

5. eating barn are cows in the

_____

6. the villagers grind did wheat

_____

7. a make does flour mill

_____

8. you do smell the cookies bakery's

_____

A future tense verb tells that an action or state of being has not begun yet, but is going to happen. Use the helping verb *will* with a main verb to form the future tense.

The animal shelter **holds** an open house. The animal shelter **will hold** an open house.

Jane **adopts** a pet rabbit. Jane **will adopt** a pet rabbit.

Complete each sentence with the future tense of the verb in parentheses ( ).

1. Many kittens _____ ready for adoption from the shelter.
   (be)

2. Jane _____ for a rabbit.
   (look)

3. A pet rabbit _____ on almost anything!
   (chew)

Rewrite each sentence in the future tense.

4. My brothers walk the dog.

   _____

5. I feed our new kitten.

   _____

6. Jane names her rabbit Flopsy.

   _____

7. Jane's mom buys a comfortable cage for the rabbit.

   _____

8. That bunny makes a lovely pet!

   _____

> Future tense verbs tell that an action or state of being has not begun yet, but is going to happen. Use the helping verb *will* with a main verb to form the future tense.
>
> The neighbors **will have** a barbeque on Saturday.
> Everyone **will eat** hamburgers and hot dogs.
> I **will go** to a dinner party instead.

Complete each sentence with a future tense verb.

1. The Gibbs family _____ neighbors over for an outdoor party.

2. Mr. Gibbs _____ hamburgers and hot dogs on the grill.

3. Jimmy _____ his special lemonade.

4. The neighborhood kids _____ games in the backyard.

5. Mrs. Gibbs _____ us how to play lawn tennis.

6. After supper, everyone _____ marshmallows over the coals.

7. Maybe we _____ fireflies.

Write three sentences in the future tense about what you will do after school today.

8. _____

_____

9. _____

_____

10. _____

_____

The present progressive tense of a verb shows that an action is happening now and will continue for a period of time.

Form the present progressive tense with the present tense of the helping verb *be* and a main verb with an *ing* ending.

I **am walking.**	We **are walking.**
You **are walking.**	You **are walking.**
She/He/It **is walking.**	They **are walking.**

Underline the present progressive form of the verb in each sentence. Then write the helping verb and the main verb in the columns.

	Helping Verb	**Main Verb**
1. I am helping my mother at work today.	_____	_____
2. Her boss is telling me about the company.	_____	_____
3. Everyone here is being nice to me.	_____	_____
4. They are offering me a job!	_____	_____

Complete each sentence with the present progressive tense of the verb in parentheses ( ).

5. The copy machine _____.
   (run)

6. People _____ coffee to their desks.
   (carry)

7. The executives _____ in the conference room.
   (meet)

8. My mom _____ to join them.
   (rush)

Fill in the bubble next to the correct answer.

1. In which sentence is the helping verb underlined?
   - Ⓐ That bird has <u>perched</u> on the fence all morning.
   - Ⓑ He <u>is</u> watching us.
   - Ⓒ He will <u>grow</u> tired of the fence.
   - Ⓓ The bird will <u>fly</u> away soon.

2. Which helping verb would you choose to form the future tense?
   - Ⓐ has
   - Ⓑ are
   - Ⓒ is
   - Ⓓ will

3. Which sentence is in the future tense?
   - Ⓐ The gardener will plant flower bulbs.
   - Ⓑ The gardener is planting flower bulbs.
   - Ⓒ The gardener plants flower bulbs.
   - Ⓓ The gardener planted flower bulbs.

4. Which tense would you use to show that an action is in progress and will continue to happen?
   - Ⓐ future tense
   - Ⓑ past tense
   - Ⓒ present tense
   - Ⓓ present progressive tense

5. Which sentence is in the present progressive tense?
   - Ⓐ Sean will cut the grass.
   - Ⓑ Sean cut the grass.
   - Ⓒ Sean is cutting the grass.
   - Ⓓ Sean cuts the grass.

Choose the right verb tense to tell or show when the action happens.

- **Present Tense:** is happening now, or happens regularly

    I **write** letters to Uncle Jack.

- **Present Progressive Tense:** is happening now and is continuing for a time

    I **am writing** a letter now.

- **Past Tense:** has happened before now and is over

    I **wrote** a letter yesterday.

- **Future Tense:** will happen sometime after now

    I **will write** again next month.

Use clue words in each sentence to decide when the action happens.
Then fill in each blank with the correct form of the verb in parentheses ( ).
Write the name of the verb tense on the line.

1. I _____ glad you called today.   _____
       (be)

2. Yesterday, I _____ a letter to you.   _____
                 (write)

3. While we talk, I _____ my clothes.   _____
                    (fold)

4. In a minute, I _____ Buddy, our dog.   _____
                  (feed)

5. Buddy _____ loudly at dinnertime.   _____
          (bark)

6. After he eats, I _____ him around the block.   _____
                    (walk)

7. Last evening, he _____ every tree on the street!   _____
                    (sniff)

8. As we speak, I _____ for his leash.   _____
                  (look)

When writing, it is important to use the same verb tense to show when the action is happening. Do not switch tenses without a reason.

Incorrect	Correct
I **wear** tap shoes to my dance class. I **wore** tights, too.	I **wear** tap shoes to my dance class. I **wear** tights, too.
Our teacher **showed** us a new step. She **teaches** us a turn, too.	Our teacher **showed** us a new step. She **taught** us a turn, too.

Write the correct form of the verb in parentheses ( ). Make sure that the tense of the verb in the second sentence matches the tense of the verb in the first sentence.

1. Frank is spinning in front of the mirror. He _____ at his reflection.
(look)

2. The dance studio has shiny floors. I _____ on them.
(slide)

3. Last year, I tripped during the final dance! Everyone _____.
(laugh)

4. I am hoping this performance will be better. I _____ more often.
(practice)

Write a second sentence that matches the tense of the first one.

5. I love music.

_____

6. I tapped my feet.

_____

7. Our teacher is playing a tuba.

_____

8. The class will applaud.

_____

Language Fundamentals • EMC 2754 • © Evan-Moor Corp.

A verb must agree in number with its subject.

- If the subject is singular, add *s* or *es* to the verb.

    The girl skips along the sidewalk.   The boy stretches the jump rope.

- If the subject is plural, do not add an ending to the verb.

    The twins skip happily.   Cats stretch in the sun.

- When the subject is *I* or *you,* do not add an ending to the verb.

    I skip home from school.   You stretch to reach the basketball hoop.

Complete each sentence with the correct form of the verb in parentheses ( ).
Then circle the correct letter to tell whether the subject is singular (S) or plural (P).

1. The kids _____ old-fashioned games at the fair.   S   P
   (enjoy)

2. Ms. Boe _____ some kids to play jacks.   S   P
   (teach)

3. Mori _____ the little red ball.   S   P
   (bounce)

4. She _____ the small metal pieces called jacks.   S   P
   (toss)

5. Other kids _____ on the sidewalk.   S   P
   (hop)

6. They _____ hopscotch all afternoon.   S   P
   (play)

7. Sometimes, you _____ on one foot in that game.   S   P
   (jump)

8. Mr. Bolski _____ me a hand-clapping game.   S   P
   (show)

9. I _____ the funny rhyme for the game.   S   P
   (chant)

10. We _____ these old-fashioned games!   S   P
    (like)

An irregular verb must agree in number with its subject.
The most common irregular verbs are *to be* and *to have*.

to be	to have
I **am** from Iowa.	I **have** a globe.
You **are** from Iowa.	You **have** a map.
She **is** from Iowa.	She **has** a photo.
We **are** from Iowa.	We **have** a map.
They **are** from Iowa.	They **have** photos.

Complete each sentence with the correct form of the verb *to be* or *to have.*

1. We _____ a family reunion every summer.

2. My cousins _____ from out of state.

3. I _____ a wonderful photo of my grandmother.

4. I _____ happy to show it to you.

5. You _____ my favorite cousin!

6. Cousin Rebecca _____ the cook this year.

7. Her potato salad _____ the best!

8. It _____ just the right amount of celery.

9. My aunts and uncles _____ great cooks, too.

10. They _____ years of experience in the kitchen.

Fill in the bubble next to the correct answer.

1. Which sentence has a verb in the correct tense?
   Ⓐ Every winter, I build a snow fort.
   Ⓑ Yesterday, I play in the snow.
   Ⓒ Next Thursday, we went to a ski lodge.
   Ⓓ I been skiing all day.

2. Which tense tells that an action will take place sometime after the present?
   Ⓐ present progressive
   Ⓑ present
   Ⓒ past
   Ⓓ future

3. In which pair of sentences are the verb tenses the same?
   Ⓐ Last night the temperature dropped. It fell below freezing.
   Ⓑ The skiing teacher shows us the trail. I followed it.
   Ⓒ It was steep. I fall once.
   Ⓓ I am riding the ski lift. It was a bit scary.

4. In which sentence does the verb agree in number with the subject?
   Ⓐ Skiers flies down the hill.
   Ⓑ A snowboarder crash into a skier.
   Ⓒ They wear casts on their legs now.
   Ⓓ They was not careful on the ski slope.

5. In which sentence does the verb agree in number with the subject?
   Ⓐ We drinks hot chocolate in the ski lodge.
   Ⓑ Frozen skiers sit beside a warm fire.
   Ⓒ I likes the snowy view from the window.
   Ⓓ I feels warm even though it is cold outside!

An adverb is a word that can describe a verb. An adverb can tell *how*, *when*, or *where*.

How	Chun cleaned her mitt **carefully.**
When	**Then** she changed her shoes.
Where	At four o'clock she walked **home.**

Circle the adverb that describes the underlined verb.

1. Chun's team <u>went</u> outside.

2. The team <u>played</u> hard.

3. But the other team soon <u>won</u> the game.

Complete each sentence with a word from the word box to describe the underlined word.

> certainly   later   sadly   then   cheerfully   tomorrow   well

4. _____ Ben <u>called</u> Chun.

5. "Your team <u>played</u> _____."

6. "Thanks," Chun <u>said</u> _____, "but we lost the game."

7. "Maybe you will <u>win</u> _____," Ben replied.

8. "We will _____ <u>try</u>," Chun answered.

9. "Good luck," Ben <u>said</u> _____.

10. "I will <u>see</u> you _____," Chun answered.

Many adverbs end in *–ly*. Adverbs that end in *–ly* often tell *how.*

Juan dove **smoothly** into the pool.

Underline the *–ly* adverb in each sentence. Circle the verb it describes.

1. The team waited patiently for the coach.

2. Everyone listened closely to the coach.

3. The coach spoke clearly so that everyone could hear.

4. The race began promptly at three o'clock.

Complete the sentences using adverbs from the word box.

carefully   happily   loudly   quickly   cheerfully   slowly

5. Juan swam _____ to the end of the pool.

6. His teammates yelled _____ to tell him they were watching.

7. Juan climbed _____ out of the pool and grabbed a towel.

8. He walked _____ along the edge of the pool.

9. Everyone clapped _____ for him.

10. Juan _____ waved to the crowd.

Some adverbs do not end in *–ly.* These adverbs often tell *when* or *where* something happens.

When   My cousin Mika is coming to visit me **tomorrow.**
Where   She likes the weather **here.**

Circle the adverb that describes each underlined verb.

1. Mika <u>called</u> me yesterday.

2. Then I <u>called</u> her.

3. Later I <u>will call</u> her again.

4. We <u>talk</u> often.

5. Sometimes we <u>talk</u> for hours.

6. Dad always <u>complains</u> about the phone bill.

Circle *where, when,* or *how* to indicate what the bolded adverb tells about the underlined verb.

7. **Today** Mom <u>said</u> Mika may come visit us.	where	when	how
8. We <u>go</u> **everywhere** we like to go.	where	when	how
9. We <u>look</u> **hard** for fun places to see.	where	when	how
10. We <u>climb</u> **nearby** at the rock gym.	where	when	how
11. **Then** we <u>buy</u> ice-cream cones.	where	when	how
12. Dad <u>takes</u> us **home.**	where	when	how

> Some adverbs describe adjectives. These adverbs can tell *how much* or *to what extent:*
>
> quite   so   such   too   very
>
> Cal draws **very** beautiful pictures. His pictures are **so** colorful!

Circle the adverb that describes the underlined adjective.

1. Cal makes such <u>great</u> paintings!

2. Some pictures are quite <u>large</u>.

3. Some pictures are so <u>small</u>!

4. Cal is a very <u>good</u> artist.

5. Nothing is too <u>hard</u> for him!

Use an adverb from the rule box to complete each sentence.

6. I try _____ hard to draw like Cal does.

7. I practice _____ many hours that my hands ache.

8. Cal is _____ helpful to me.

9. My pictures are not _____ as colorful as his are.

10. I like _____ peaceful pictures.

11. Some colors are _____ bright for my paintings.

12. My paintings are _____ calming.

Name _____

> Add *–er* or *–est* to some adverbs to make comparisons.
>
> • *–er* = more
>
>   Sun climbs **higher** than some kids in our class.
>
> • *–est* = most
>
>   Beth climbs **highest** of all.

Complete each sentence by adding *–er* or *–est* to the adverb in parentheses ( ).

1. Of all my friends, Sue lives _____ to the school.
   (near)

2. Troy's house is _____ on the hill than his neighbor's house.
   (high)

3. Pat lives _____ to my house than Maria.
   (close)

4. Of everyone I know, Brad's house is the _____ to the beach.
   (close)

5. I live _____ to Sue than Tina does.
   (near)

Tell about where you and your friends live. Use adverbs from the word box.

> closer   closest   nearer   nearest

6. _____

   _____.

7. _____

   _____.

8. _____

   _____.

    Language Fundamentals • EMC 2754 • © Evan-Moor Corp.

To compare adverbs with two or more syllables, use these words:

More or Most	Lisa works **more** independently than Megan. Sam works the **most** independently of all.
Less or Least	Taylor works **less** independently than many students. Jill works the **least** independently of all.

Underline the adverbs that compare.

1. Lisa plays computer games more often than Sam does.

2. As the game speeds up, she moves her fingers more rapidly.

3. The top levels of the game move the most rapidly of all.

4. Sam plays computer games less often than Lisa does.

5. His little brother plays the least often of all.

Write a comparative form of the adverb in parentheses ( ). Use *more, most, less,* or *least.*

6. I go to the carnival _____ than my sister does.
    (often)

7. My brother goes _____ than I do.
    (often)

8. From here I can see the rides _____ than from home.
    (clearly)

9. I can see them _____ from school than from other places.
    (clearly)

10. We all go to the carnival _____ on clear nights.
    (frequently)

Comparing with Adverbs

> Negatives are words that mean "no" or "not."
>
> There is **no** way to get there from here.
>
> That place is **nowhere** near here.
>
> I **never** miss the bus.
>
> I do **not** like to be late.

Circle the negative word in each sentence.

1. I did not catch the school bus this morning.

2. By the time I got there, it was nowhere in sight.

3. That had never happened before.

4. There was no time for me to walk.

Write a negative word in each blank.

> no   not   never   nowhere

5. Kit could _____ find her cat, Cleo.

6. Cleo _____ left home alone.

7. Kit found _____ sign of her cat anywhere.

8. She could think of _____ else to look.

9. Kit had _____ been so worried!

10. Kit could _____ believe it when she saw Cleo under the house.

Name _____

Fill in the bubble next to the correct answer.

1. Which adverb describes the underlined verb?
   Our team <u>played</u> hard and won the game.

   Ⓐ team

   Ⓑ hard

   Ⓒ won

   Ⓓ game

2. Mark the adverb that tells how.
   We quickly chose several kinds of pizza.

   Ⓐ quickly

   Ⓑ several

   Ⓒ pizza

   Ⓓ of

3. Which adverb describes an adjective?
   We planned so many trips.

   Ⓐ planned

   Ⓑ so

   Ⓒ many

   Ⓓ trips

4. Which adverb compares?
   The trip will take her farther from home than she traveled last year.

   Ⓐ home

   Ⓑ from

   Ⓒ farther

   Ⓓ last

5. Which word is a negative?
   Tanya and Tina never sit together in class.

   Ⓐ sit

   Ⓑ class

   Ⓒ never

   Ⓓ together

A preposition is used to show the relationship of a noun or pronoun to another word in a sentence.

above	beside	inside	to
around	during	on	toward
at	for	over	under
behind	in	through	upon

We are riding **on** the bus.

I am sitting **between** two friends.

We see a sign **with** a big fish.

The bus is headed **toward** the sign.

Underline the preposition in each sentence.

1. Our class is taking a field trip to the aquarium.

2. There are many different fish inside the big tanks.

3. We see brightly colored fish behind the glass.

4. A huge shark appears above the smaller fish.

5. The fish scatter as the shark dives toward them.

6. A baby whale swims beside its mother.

7. There are tiny sea horses galloping under the water.

8. There are sea stars climbing over rocks.

9. Outside we watch dolphins jumping through hoops.

10. We see many fascinating creatures during our visit.

   Language Fundamentals • EMC 2754 • © Evan-Moor Corp.

Name _____

A prepositional phrase is made up of a preposition, the noun or pronoun that comes after the preposition, and any words in between. The noun or pronoun is called the object of the preposition.

Prepositional Phrase

The dog is hiding **under** the **bed**.

Preposition   Object of the
                   Preposition

Prepositional Phrase

The dog will not go **with us**.

Preposition   Object of the
               Preposition

Choose a word from the word box to make a prepositional phrase in each sentence. Circle the object of each preposition.

behind	for	beside	during	to
around	inside	over	at	from

1. Our dog, Sam, always knows when he is going _____ the vet.

2. We have to fight to get him _____ the car.

3. One time, he jumped _____ the fence and ran away.

4. Another time, he tried to hide _____ the stove and got stuck!

5. He whines and cries _____ the whole trip.

6. But if we are just driving _____ town, he is happy.

7. When we are going away, he doesn't mind staying _____ the kennel.

8. Somehow he knows when it is time _____ a checkup!

9. He is different _____ our other dog, Sandy.

10. Sandy will sit _____ me when it is time to visit the vet.

Name _____

A prepositional phrase is made up of a preposition, the noun or pronoun that comes after the preposition, and any words in between.

Some prepositional phrases describe nouns.

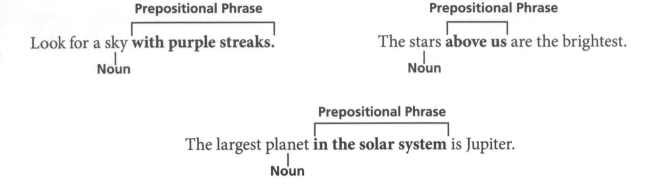

Prepositional Phrase

Look for a sky **with purple streaks.**
Noun

Prepositional Phrase

The stars **above us** are the brightest.
Noun

Prepositional Phrase

The largest planet **in the solar system** is Jupiter.
Noun

Underline the prepositional phrase in each sentence. Circle the noun it describes.

1. The moonlight on the water is awesome.

2. The waves from our boat sparkle in the light.

3. Folklore states that a ring around the moon means bad weather.

4. I can make a wish upon a star tonight.

5. I see a constellation with a familiar shape.

6. Those stars in a straight line belong to the Big Dipper.

7. The constellation Cassiopeia is beside the Big Dipper and Orion.

8. The constellation above the North Star is often Cassiopeia.

9. The most recognizable constellation in the Southern Hemisphere is the Southern Cross.

10. I hope to find an undiscovered star in the sky.

A prepositional phrase is made up of a preposition, the noun or pronoun that is the object of the preposition, and any words in between.

Some prepositional phrases describe verbs. They can tell *how*, *where*, or *when*.

Prepositional Phrase

Many settlers came **in covered wagons.**
Verb

Prepositional Phrase

Our town was built **beside a river.**
Verb

Prepositional Phrase

The population increased **through the years.**
Verb

Choose a word from the word box to complete each sentence. Underline the prepositional phrase. You may use a word more than once. Write *how*, *when*, or *where* above the phrase to explain what it tells. The first one has been done for you.

around   along   beside   between   during   in   over   through   with

1. Our local history fair begins _____ *when* in _____ less than a week.

2. We have different exhibits to set up _____ our classroom.

3. One exhibit explains life long ago _____ a diorama.

4. There is a timeline of the town running _____ one wall.

5. We want to show how the town changed _____ the years.

6. Students are placing old maps _____ new ones to show those changes.

7. We will have many classes visiting _____ morning and afternoon hours.

8. We're proud that we are sharing our knowledge _____ others.

Fill in the bubble next to the correct answer.

1. Which sentence has a preposition?

Ⓐ Apples and bananas are my favorite fruits.

Ⓑ I will eat apples anytime.

Ⓒ Can I have a banana?

Ⓓ I like bananas on my cereal.

2. Identify the prepositional phrase in this sentence.
   Those kids beside the fountain are my classmates.

Ⓐ Those kids

Ⓑ beside

Ⓒ beside the fountain

Ⓓ are my classmates

3. Identify the object of the preposition in this sentence.
   The water is rising rapidly under the bridge.

Ⓐ water

Ⓑ rapidly

Ⓒ under

Ⓓ bridge

4. Which prepositional phrase describes a noun?

Ⓐ This plant <u>behind the tall tree</u> is not getting enough light.

Ⓑ A vine is growing <u>down the chimney</u> and could catch fire.

Ⓒ Many flowers look best <u>in the morning</u>.

Ⓓ The roses are climbing <u>up the wall</u>.

5. Which prepositional phrase tells where?

Ⓐ The library is getting a painting <u>from a famous artist</u>.

Ⓑ We can visit the library <u>in a few weeks</u> to see the painting.

Ⓒ The painting is kept hidden <u>from the public</u>.

Ⓓ The painting will be displayed <u>above the librarian's desk</u>.

 Language Fundamentals • EMC 2754 • © Evan-Moor Corp.

> A sentence is a group of words that express a complete thought.
> A statement is a sentence that tells something. It ends with a period (.).
>
> Winter is cold and flu season.
>
> I have a cold.

Answer each question with a statement. Make sure that each statement is a complete sentence that begins with a capital letter and ends with a period.

1. When do people usually go on vacation?

   _____

2. In what season do the leaves fall from the trees?

   _____

3. In what season do the first buds blossom?

   _____

4. Where would you like to go on vacation?

   _____

Write a statement on each topic below. Make sure that each statement is a complete sentence that begins with a capital letter and ends with a period.

5. (Saturdays) _____

   _____

6. (dessert)_____

   _____

A question is a sentence that asks something. It ends with a question mark (?).

Are you having fun at the amusement park?
Have you seen the roller coaster?

Many questions begin with one of these words:

who   what   where   when   why   how

Write a question that might be followed by the given answer. Be sure to begin the question with a capital letter and end it with a question mark.

1. Question: _____

   Answer: It is called a Ferris wheel because it was invented by Mr. G. W. G. Ferris.

2. Question: _____

   Answer: Mr. Ferris invented his famous ride in the year 1893.

3. Question: _____

   Answer: My favorite ride is the tilt-a-whirl.

4. Question: _____

   Answer: I rode it four times yesterday.

Write a question about each subject.

5. (inventions) _____

6. (roller coasters) _____

7. (picnics) _____

8. (cotton candy) _____

> An exclamation is a sentence that expresses a strong feeling. It ends with an exclamation point (*!*).
>
> The circus is coming to town! Here comes the parade!
>
> **Sometimes an exclamation is just one or two words long.**
>
> Wow!   Look!   Oh, no!

One of the sentences in each pair is an exclamation and the other is a statement. Add the correct punctuation mark to the end of each sentence.

1. Uncle Fred is taking us to the circus ___ What fun it will be ___

2. I can't wait ___ We're going on Saturday ___

3. I have our tickets ready ___ We are finally here ___

4. Oh, listen ___ The band is starting to play ___

Describe each picture with an exclamation.

5. _____

_____

_____

_____

6. _____

_____

_____

_____

An imperative sentence gives a command. It ends with a period (.).

Close the door.
Open the windows.

Some imperative sentences contain a courtesy word such as *please*.

Please come quickly.
Clean your room, **please**.

Underline the imperative sentences.

1. This room is a mess! Pick up your socks.

2. Is that a candy wrapper under your bed? Throw it away.

3. Hang up the clean clothes. I will wash these.

4. Next, we'll organize this closet. Open the door, please.

Study the picture of the messy room. Write two imperative sentences an adult could be saying to the child.

5. _____

_____

6. _____

_____

> A sentence is a group of words that express a complete thought. There are four kinds of sentences.
>
> - A statement tells something. It ends with a period (.).
>   Enrico Caruso was a famous singer**.**
>
> - A question asks something. It ends with a question mark (?).
>   Have you heard of him**?**
>
> - An exclamation shows strong feeling. It ends with an exclamation point (*!*).
>   He had a fantastic voice**!**
>
> - An imperative sentence gives a command. It ends with a period (.).
>   Play this recording**.**

What kind of sentence is it? Write *statement*, *question*, *imperative*, or *exclamation* on the line. Then add the correct punctuation mark to the sentence.

1. Hand me that CD _____

2. Caruso was an opera singer _____

3. Do you like opera _____

4. I love it _____

5. My sister hates it _____

6. Listen closely to Caruso's voice _____

7. An opera tells a story with music _____

8. Would you like to listen to my favorite opera _____

9. My favorite opera is *The Magic Flute* _____

10. How beautiful it is _____

A group of words that is punctuated like a sentence, but does not have both a subject and a predicate, is called a sentence fragment. A fragment is not a complete sentence. It does not express a complete thought.

Sentence Fragment	Ate dinner in a restaurant last night.
Sentence Fragment	My parents.
Complete Sentence	My parents ate dinner in a restaurant last night.

Label each group of words below as either a complete sentence or a fragment.

1. Last Saturday night at my house. _____

2. Our big brother was in charge. _____

3. We watched a movie. _____

4. About two kids and their parents on Mars. _____

5. The story was science fiction. _____

6. Pizza and a big salad with lots of crunchy vegetables. _____

7. We ate pizza and salad. _____

8. Had pepperoni and mushrooms. _____

9. Climbed into bed very late! _____

10. Our parents came home even later! _____

A sentence fragment is <u>not</u> a complete sentence. It does <u>not</u> express a complete thought.

Sentence Fragment
A tasty stew of beef, carrots, potatoes, and onions.
Juan and Ella in the kitchen.
Prepared the table for dinner.

To turn a fragment into a complete sentence, add missing information. Make sure that the sentence has both a subject and a predicate.

Subject	Predicate
A tasty stew	simmers on the stove.
Juan and Ella	stirred the pot in the kitchen.
They	set the table for dinner.

Turn each sentence fragment below into a complete sentence by adding missing information. Write the sentence on the line.

1. My mother and father in the dining room.

   _____

2. Opened the door for our guests.

   _____

3. Mr. Hirata and his daughter.

   _____

4. Heard the doorbell ring again.

   _____

5. Everyone at the table.

   _____

Fill in the bubble next to the correct answer.

1. Which group of words is a fragment?
   - Ⓐ What was that sound?
   - Ⓑ I'm scared!
   - Ⓒ Tell a funny story, please.
   - Ⓓ Late at night in the backyard.

2. Which example turns this fragment into a complete sentence?
   With the flashlight.
   - Ⓐ With the flashlight, Grace and I.
   - Ⓑ Grace and I with the flashlight.
   - Ⓒ I explored the backyard with the flashlight.
   - Ⓓ In the backyard with the flashlight.

3. Read the sentence. Choose the correct sentence type.
   Don't scratch that mosquito bite.
   - Ⓐ statement
   - Ⓑ question
   - Ⓒ exclamation
   - Ⓓ imperative

4. Read the sentence. Choose the correct sentence type.
   That owl scared me!
   - Ⓐ statement
   - Ⓑ question
   - Ⓒ exclamation
   - Ⓓ imperative

5. Which sentence ends with the correct punctuation mark?
   - Ⓐ The lotion smells a little funny?
   - Ⓑ Has the itching stopped?
   - Ⓒ Mosquitoes are common in the summer!
   - Ⓓ Stop scratching, please?

> Every sentence has two parts, a subject and a predicate.
>
> - The subject tells who or what the sentence is about.
>
>   **Our school** is having a fire drill today.
>   When will the **fire alarm** ring?
>
> - The predicate tells what the subject is or does.
>
>   The alarm **is very loud!**
>   Everyone **leaves the building.**

Circle the subject and underline the predicate of each sentence.

1. Safety is very important at our school.

2. The exit doors are clearly marked.

3. We practice leaving the building in orderly lines.

4. Teachers lead the way out of the building.

Complete each sentence below by adding either a subject or a predicate from the word box.

you	won a fire safety award
enter burning buildings	Fire

5. _____ is a dangerous thing.

6. Firefighters _____.

7. Can _____ imagine doing that?

8. Our school _____!

Name _____

> A complete sentence has two parts, a subject and a predicate.

- The subject names the person, place, or thing that the sentence is about.
- The predicate tells what the subject is or does.

Subject	Predicate
The storm	came without warning.
The funnel of wind	swirled violently.

Draw one line under the subject and two lines under the predicate in each sentence.

1. The whole family listens to the radio each morning.

2. The radio sits on the kitchen counter.

3. Jeremy waits for the weather report.

4. The forecast calls for rain in the afternoon.

5. An umbrella will be necessary.

Read each sentence. Then write each sentence part on the lines below.

6. The dark clouds gathered over the playground.

    Subject: _____ Predicate: _____

7. All of the children watched the clouds.

    Subject: _____ Predicate: _____

8. The rain is falling hard now.

    Subject: _____ Predicate: _____

> The subject of a sentence tells who or what.
>
> Frogs live in this pond.
> **Subject**
>
> The predicate tells what the subject does or is.
>
> The water in the pond is cold.
> **Predicate**

Answer each question below.

The female frogs lay eggs in the spring.

1. **Subject:** What is the sentence about?   _____

2. **Predicate:** What do they do?   _____

The eggs hatch in the water.

3. **Subject:** What is the sentence about?   _____

4. **Predicate:** What do they do?   _____

A tadpole hatches from each egg.

5. **Subject:** What is the sentence about?   _____

6. **Predicate:** What does the subject do?   _____

Every adult frog started life as a tadpole.

7. **Subject:** What is the sentence about?   _____

8. **Predicate:** What did the subject do?   _____

Subjects and Predicates   **95**

Name _____

> Every complete sentence has a subject. In a sentence that is a command, the subject is always *you.* The subject *you* is usually not stated in the sentence but is understood to be the subject.
>
> (You) Find the book in the library.
>
> (You) Please return the book on time.

What is the subject of each sentence below? Write it on the line.

1. Gently turn the pages of that old book.   _____

2. Please treat it with care.   _____

3. The book is very rare.   _____

4. Look at the lovely old pictures.   _____

Write four commands that you might hear from a librarian. Write the understood subject of each sentence on the second line.

5. _____   _____

   _____

6. _____   _____

   _____

7. _____   _____

   _____

8. _____   _____

   _____

Name _____

> Every sentence has a subject. The complete subject includes all the words that tell about the subject. The simple subject is the most important word of the complete subject, the noun.
>
> **Simple Subject**
>
> **My closest friend** moved away.
>
> **Complete Subject**
>
> **Simple Subject**
>
> **Her big family** lives in another state now.
>
> **Complete Subject**

Underline the complete subject of each sentence and circle the simple subject.

1. A huge truck pulled up to the front door of Debbie's house.

2. The movers carried out box after box.

3. Movers with big muscles lifted the living room sofa.

4. The driver of the truck looked at a map.

5. Debbie's new address is written in my address book.

Complete the underlined subject in each sentence by choosing a simple subject from the word box.

> home   elevator   e-mail   view   apartment

6. The first _____ from Debbie has arrived.

7. Her new _____ is in a big city.

8. An _____ in a tall building is her new home.

9. An _____ takes her to the top floor.

10. The _____ from her bedroom window must be amazing!

The simple subject is the most important word in the complete subject.

- Sometimes the simple subject is the same as the complete subject.

Photographers aim their cameras at the star of the movie.

Complete / \ Simple
Subject   Subject

- Sometimes the simple subject is made up of two or more words that name a person or a place.

New York City is home to many famous people.

Complete   Simple
Subject   Subject

Underline the complete subject in each sentence and circle the simple subject. Sometimes the complete subject and the simple subject are the same.

1. Lee Ann Michaels wants to be a movie star.

2. She takes dance classes and acting classes.

3. The entire class went to see her in a play.

4. The biggest part in the play belonged to Lee Ann.

5. Hollywood, California, may be Lee Ann's home someday.

Write three sentences about what you might like to do when you grow up. Underline the complete subject and circle the simple subject in each sentence.

6. _____

_____

7. _____

_____

8. _____

_____

Every sentence has a predicate.

- The complete predicate includes all of the words in the predicate.
- The simple predicate is the verb. It is the most important word in the predicate.

```
              Simple
             Predicate
              ┌─┐
The children race across the backyard.
             └─────────────────────┘
             Complete Predicate
```

Underline the complete predicate in each sentence. Write the simple predicate on the line.

1. The children in the neighborhood race through the backyards. _____

2. One girl begins a game of basketball after a game of tag. _____

3. An older boy chooses sides for a game of softball. _____

4. We went inside after sundown. _____

5. It was a nice evening. _____

Choose a simple predicate from the word box to complete each sentence. Then underline the complete predicate.

> mows   apologized   clipped   smells   dug

6. Mr. Samuels _____ his lawn.

7. The freshly cut grass _____ good.

8. Last night, Mrs. Samuels _____ the hedges.

9. Our dog _____ a deep hole in the Samuels' garden once.

10. I sincerely _____ for Gigi, our poodle.

Every sentence has a predicate.

- When the verb is made up of a main verb and a helping verb, together those words make up the simple predicate.

Simple Predicate

The house **is burning** out of control!

Complete Predicate

- Sometimes the complete predicate and the simple predicate are the same.

Simple Predicate

The fire trucks **are coming**.

Complete Predicate

Underline the complete predicate and circle the simple predicate.

1. The American Red Cross will help.

2. That organization was started by Clara Barton in 1881.

3. She modeled the American Red Cross after the International Red Cross.

4. In Europe, Clara Barton had seen the good work of that organization.

5. The American Red Cross will bring supplies in times of disaster.

Write the simple predicate after each sentence.

6. The family across the street has lost everything in a fire. _____

7. The Red Cross is finding clothes for them. _____

8. They will stay at a friend's house for a while. _____

9. The family will build a new house in the same place. _____

10. I am giving the younger kids some books and toys. _____

Fill in the bubble next to the correct answer.

1. In which sentence is the complete subject underlined?

   Ⓐ My big sister <u>wants to be a dentist</u>.

   Ⓑ <u>Someday</u> she will go to dental school.

   Ⓒ <u>My big brother</u> wants to be a veterinarian.

   Ⓓ I want to be <u>a pilot</u>.

2. In which sentence is only the simple subject underlined?

   Ⓐ I change <u>my mind</u> often.

   Ⓑ Yesterday, I wanted to be a <u>barber</u>.

   Ⓒ <u>Barbers</u> cut hair and talk to people.

   Ⓓ <u>My next-door neighbor</u> is a barber.

3. Which sentence is correctly divided into subject and predicate?

   Ⓐ Uncle Ralph went / to barber school.

   Ⓑ He / has his own shop now.

   Ⓒ A red and white / pole hangs outside.

   Ⓓ The pole spins / around.

4. Which pronoun is always the subject of a command?

   Ⓐ You

   Ⓑ I

   Ⓒ They

   Ⓓ He

5. In which sentence is only the simple predicate underlined?

   Ⓐ Dr. Anne Kennedy <u>graduated from our school many years ago</u>.

   Ⓑ She came to talk to us about her <u>job</u>.

   Ⓒ At the hospital, Dr. Kennedy <u>operates</u> on people.

   Ⓓ Maybe I'll <u>be a doctor someday</u>.

A simple sentence contains a subject and a predicate. A simple sentence can be short or long.

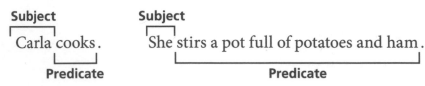

Subject

Carla cooks.

Predicate

Subject

She stirs a pot full of potatoes and ham.

Predicate

Write each sentence part on the lines below.

1. Italian food is my favorite kind of food.

_____   _____
      complete subject   complete predicate

2. My grandmother makes Polish food.

_____   _____
      complete subject   complete predicate

3. I like stuffed cabbage.

_____   _____
      complete subject   complete predicate

4. Peanut butter sandwiches are good, too.

_____   _____
      complete subject   complete predicate

Write your own simple sentences about your favorite foods. Then circle the complete subject and underline the complete predicate.

5. _____

6. _____

7. _____

8. _____

Language Fundamentals • EMC 2754 • © Evan-Moor Corp.

Some sentences have parts that are joined by connecting words called conjunctions. One kind of conjunction connects two words, two phrases, or two simple sentences.

and   but   or   so   yet

I am excited to go camping **and** hiking.

I will sleep in a tent **or** under the stars.

It will be very dark at night, **but** I won't be afraid.

Circle the conjunction in each sentence.

1. I would like a clown or a juggler to entertain at my birthday party.

2. I want a performer, so I will look in the phone book under "Entertainers."

3. A clown could do tricks or make those cool balloon animals.

4. I love clowns, but I know some kids think they are silly.

5. I've seen a juggler toss balls in the air and balance plates on a stick.

6. A juggler would be amazing to watch, yet I would still like a clown.

7. I cannot decide which I want, so I'll ask to have two performers at my party!

8. My birthday will be funny and entertaining!

9. Next, I need to decide if I want a chocolate or white cake.

10. Chocolate is my favorite, but some people only like white.

> You can use the conjunction *and* to connect two simple sentences. When you do this, you form a compound sentence. Place a comma before the conjunction.
>
> | **Simple Sentences** | I love music. I play the guitar. |
> | **Compound Sentence** | I love music, **and** I play the guitar. |
>
> | **Simple Sentences** | I played that song yesterday. Today I will play it again. |
> | **Compound Sentence** | I played that song yesterday, **and** today I will play it again. |

Rewrite each sentence pair below as a compound sentence with the conjunction *and*. Place a comma before the conjunction.

1. I tune my guitar. I play it every day.

   _____

2. It is easy to strum. It is easy to play the chords.

   _____

3. You can listen to me play. You can tell me what you think.

   _____

   _____

4. Why is the dog howling? Why did the cat run away?

   _____

   _____

Using the conjunction *and* and a comma, write your own compound sentence about playing an instrument.

5. _____

   _____

You can use the conjunction *but* to connect two simple sentences. This forms a compound sentence that compares or contrasts. Place a comma before the conjunction.

Simple Sentences	I like all kinds of stories.	Mysteries are my favorite kind.
Compound Sentence	I like all kinds of stories, **but** mysteries are my favorite kind.	

Join a simple sentence from Box A to a simple sentence from Box B. Build a compound sentence using the conjunction *but* and a comma. Write each compound sentence on the line.

Box A
• I want to play with my cat.
• He was in the living room a minute ago.
• Clues are hard to find.
• I see a tail sticking out from behind the sofa.

Box B
• He is not in the living room now.
• It belongs to the dog.
• I don't know where he is.
• I keep looking.

1. _____

_____

2. _____

_____

3. _____

_____

4. _____

_____

> You can use the conjunction *or* to connect two simple sentences. This forms a compound sentence that shows choice. Place a comma before the conjunction.
>
> **Simple Sentences**   You may have a turkey sandwich. You may have chili.
> **Compound Sentence**   You may have a turkey sandwich, **or** you may have chili.

Complete the compound sentences below by adding the conjunction *or* and a comma.

1. You can buy your lunch in the cafeteria _____ you can bring it from home.

2. My mother gives me a deviled egg in my lunch _____ she gives me some cheese.

3. I eat the deviled egg first _____ I eat it after my sandwich.

Create compound sentences using the conjunction *or*. Remember to use a comma.

4. We could take the bus downtown _____

_____

5. We could eat at Burger Barn _____

_____

6. You might decide to go shopping _____

_____

7. I will buy a cookbook _____

_____

8. I want to eat an ice-cream cone _____

_____

Fill in the bubble next to the correct answer.

1. Which group of words is a simple sentence?
   Ⓐ Costume parties are fun, and I am planning one.
   Ⓑ After some thought.
   Ⓒ My parents will help me plan the party.
   Ⓓ Apples and potato chips with dip.

2. Which sentence is a compound sentence?
   Ⓐ Tameeka is going to dress as a scientist.
   Ⓑ She will wear a lab coat, and she will carry a microscope.
   Ⓒ I decided on a great costume after I talked to Tameeka.
   Ⓓ I will dress as a police officer.

3. Which sentence has a conjunction?
   Ⓐ Jacob and Ethan are my best friends.
   Ⓑ Jacob is one of Ethan's friends.
   Ⓒ I have two good friends at school.
   Ⓓ Many of my friends do not go to my school.

4. Choose the example that combines the short sentences correctly.
   The drive to the desert was long. The scenery was beautiful.
   Ⓐ The drive to the desert was long but the scenery was beautiful.
   Ⓑ The drive to the desert was long and the scenery was beautiful.
   Ⓒ The drive to the desert was long, the scenery was beautiful.
   Ⓓ The drive to the desert was long, but the scenery was beautiful.

5. Choose the example that combines the short sentences correctly.
   I could buy that green shirt. I could buy the red jacket.
   Ⓐ I could buy that green shirt, or I could buy the red jacket.
   Ⓑ I could buy that green shirt but the red jacket.
   Ⓒ I could buy that green shirt or I could buy the red jacket.
   Ⓓ I could buy that green shirt, I could buy the red jacket.

The conjunctions listed below can be used to join two simple sentences. The conjunction helps to show how one part of the sentence relates to the other. No comma is needed before the conjunction.

after   before   if   once   since   until

I cannot play video games. I finish my homework.

I cannot play video games **until** I finish my homework.

Draw a line under each simple sentence and circle the conjunction.

1. I fixed a snack for myself after I came home from school.

2. I ate an apple before I fixed some crackers and cheese.

3. I'll start my homework once I clean up my mess.

4. My dad turned off the TV since it was a school night.

5. On Friday evenings, my family watches a movie before we go to bed.

6. I like to read in bed after the movie is over.

7. I read my book until I fall asleep.

8. My mom will turn out my light if she sees me sleeping.

9. Dad cooks a big breakfast on Saturdays since he doesn't have to go to work.

10. I stay in bed until my dog jumps on me!

11. He jumps on me because I'm the person who feeds him.

12. Then we go downstairs before all the food is gone.

Language Fundamentals • EMC 2754 • © Evan-Moor Corp.

The conjunctions listed below can be used to join two simple sentences. The conjunction helps to show how one part of the sentence relates to the other. No comma is needed before the conjunction.

because   unless   when   whenever   while

We will go to the lake for the holiday. We go there every year.

We will go to the lake for the holiday **because** we go there every year.

Draw a line under each simple sentence and circle the conjunction.

1. I get excited about the Fourth of July when school is out in June.

2. My sister makes the invitations to our party while I make the decorations.

3. We always have a picnic outdoors unless there is a terrible rainstorm.

4. We have a picnic inside on the floor whenever there is a storm.

5. My aunt always makes a red, white, and blue cake because baking is her specialty.

6. We walk to the park when the picnic is over.

7. We get there early because there is always a big crowd for the fireworks.

8. Everyone looks up and cheers when the fireworks start flashing!

9. My dad always claps whenever the band plays a march.

10. He dances with my mom while the band marches past us!

The conjunctions listed below can be used to join two simple sentences. The conjunction helps to show how one part of the sentence relates to the other. No comma is needed before the conjunction.

after	because	before
if	once	since
unless	until	when
whenever	while	where

I am reading about Egypt. I am interested in pyramids.

I am reading about Egypt **because** I am interested in pyramids.

Tourists climb the pyramids. They ride camels into the desert.

Tourists climb the pyramids **after** they ride camels into the desert.

Choose the conjunction from the rule box to correctly combine the parts of each sentence.

1. The pyramids are amazing _____ they are so huge and so old.

2. The builders did not have big cranes _____ the pyramids were built.

3. I have looked at many photographs _____ I started reading about Egypt.

4. I decided to study Egypt _____ I saw a photograph of the Sphinx.

5. I am going to make a model of the Sphinx _____ I present my report to the class.

6. I learned about a famous dam in Egypt _____ I was doing my research.

7. Egypt's electricity supply doubled _____ the High Dam was built at Aswan.

8. I will be an expert on Egypt _____ I read all these books!

Combine short sentences by moving key words or phrases from one sentence to another.

Short Sentences	Alex read a book. It was about a mysterious house.
Combined	Alex read a book about a mysterious house.
Short Sentences	The old house had an attic. The attic had dark windows.
Combined	The old house had an attic with dark windows.

Combine each sentence pair by moving words and phrases from one sentence to the other. Sometimes you may need to add words.

1. The mysterious house was old. It had squeaky doors.

   _____

2. The house was hidden. It was hidden by thick trees.

   _____

3. Slowly, the children approached the house. They took their dog.

   _____

4. Their dog barked. He barked at the cat in the window.

   _____

5. Ms. Kinley lived in the house. She lived with her cat.

   _____

6. Ms. Kinley needed help. She needed help cleaning out her mysterious attic.

   _____

Fill in the bubble next to the correct answer. Choose the example that combines the short sentences correctly.

1. *The class painted a mural. We painted it for the school office.*

   Ⓐ The class painted a mural for the school office.

   Ⓑ The class painted a mural, we painted it for the school office.

   Ⓒ The class painted a mural and put it in the school office.

   Ⓓ The class painted a mural in the school office.

2. *The leaves change colors in the fall. The pine needles stay green.*

   Ⓐ The leaves change colors in the fall, the pine needles stay green.

   Ⓑ The leaves change colors in the fall or the pine needles stay green.

   Ⓒ The leaves change colors in the fall while the pine needles stay green.

   Ⓓ The leaves change colors in the fall the pine needles stay green.

3. *Jenny's shirt has buttons. The buttons are round.*

   Ⓐ Jenny's shirt has round buttons.

   Ⓑ Jenny's shirt has buttons and they are round.

   Ⓒ Jenny's shirt has buttons, while the buttons are round.

   Ⓓ Jenny's shirt has buttons while they are round.

4. *Her dog snores. It has a short nose.*

   Ⓐ Her dog snores, or it has a short nose.

   Ⓑ Her dog snores, it has a short nose.

   Ⓒ Her dog's short nose snores.

   Ⓓ Her dog snores because it has a short nose.

5. *Ryan went to a movie. He ate popcorn.*

   Ⓐ Ryan went to a movie while he ate popcorn.

   Ⓑ Ryan went to a movie, but he ate popcorn.

   Ⓒ Ryan went to a movie where he ate popcorn.

   Ⓓ Ryan went to a movie and popcorn.

   Language Fundamentals • EMC 2754 • © Evan-Moor Corp.

Name _____

25

A run-on sentence is made up of two or more sentences that run together without punctuation or a connecting word. You can correct a run-on sentence by forming two sentences.

Run-on Sentence	The ice on the pond is solid Kenny wants to go ice-skating.
Correction	The ice on the pond is solid. Kenny wants to go ice-skating.
Run-on Sentence	He carries his skates an extra scarf is a good idea, too.
Correction	He carries his skates. An extra scarf is a good idea, too.

Correct each run-on sentence by dividing it into two simple sentences. Write the new sentences on the line.

1. The ice on the pond is thick we can skate safely.

   _____

2. There is Mr. Graff he is doing a fancy turn.

   _____

3. Sherry and Tyler hold hands they skate around and around.

   _____

   _____

4. The littlest kids wobble that one keeps falling down.

   _____

5. Some moms and dads have built a fire we can get warm.

   _____

   _____

© Evan-Moor Corp. • EMC 2754 • Language Fundamentals

Name _____

> You can correct a run-on sentence by forming two sentences.

Run-on Sentence	Mother's Day is coming I have five dollars to spend.
Correction	Mother's Day is coming. I have five dollars to spend.
Run-on Sentence	My mom likes flowers roses are her favorite.
Correction	My mom likes flowers. Roses are her favorite.

Correct each run-on sentence by dividing it into two simple sentences.
Write the new sentences on the line.

1. I made a special gift for Mother's Day I worked a long time on it.

_____

_____

2. I want to show my mom how much I appreciate her I made a giant card.

_____

_____

3. The card is as tall as my dad he will help me hold it.

_____

_____

4. I hope she loves the card I want this to be her best Mother's Day yet.

_____

_____

You can correct a run-on sentence by adding a comma and a conjunction such as *and, but,* or *or* to make a compound sentence.

Run-on	David designed the costumes Mark designed the stage sets.
Correction	David designed the costumes, **and** Mark designed the stage sets.
Run-on	Leslie will audition for the play she doesn't want the lead.
Correction	Leslie will audition for the play, **but** she doesn't want the lead.

Rewrite each run-on sentence correctly by adding a comma and a conjunction.

1. Leslie likes to sing she can't dance.

_____

2. Jackson wants the lead in the play he has a good chance of getting it.

_____

_____

3. Jackson can sing he can dance, too.

_____

4. Everyone wants to hear Jackson sing he has a sore throat.

_____

_____

5. He will rest his voice he will be ready to sing tomorrow.

_____

_____

Name _____

Fill in the bubble next to the correct answer.

1. Which answer best corrects the run-on sentence?
   My cousins and I love to race go-karts we go every weekend.

   Ⓐ My cousins and I love to race go-karts and we go every weekend.

   Ⓑ My cousins and I love to race go-karts. We go every weekend.

   Ⓒ My cousins and I love to race go-karts, we go every weekend.

   Ⓓ My cousins and I love to race go-karts, so, we go every weekend.

2. Which answer best corrects the run-on sentence?
   I love to cook my favorite dish to cook is spaghetti.

   Ⓐ I love to cook, and my favorite dish to cook is spaghetti.

   Ⓑ I love to cook my favorite dish. To cook is spaghetti.

   Ⓒ I love to cook, my favorite dish to cook is spaghetti.

   Ⓓ I love to cook, and, my favorite dish to cook is spaghetti.

3. Which answer best corrects the run-on sentence?
   Butterflies are beautiful they don't live very long.

   Ⓐ Butterflies are beautiful but they don't live very long.

   Ⓑ Butterflies are beautiful They don't live very long.

   Ⓒ Butterflies are beautiful, but, they don't live very long.

   Ⓓ Butterflies are beautiful, but they don't live very long.

4. Which sentence is a run-on sentence?

   Ⓐ Our school band is playing tonight it will be fun.

   Ⓑ I practiced every day, and I improved my skills.

   Ⓒ I will play a solo tonight. I am so excited!

   Ⓓ Both my parents will be there to watch me play.

5. Which sentence is a run-on sentence?

   Ⓐ I love writing stories, but it can be difficult.

   Ⓑ I can get stuck and not be able to think of anything.

   Ⓒ I keep writing when that happens I write anything I can imagine.

   Ⓓ Writing anything helps with writer's block!

Name _____

> Capitalize the first word in a sentence.
>
> **It** happened a long time ago.
>
> **Do** you think that one small event can change your life?

Draw three lines under the first letter of the word that needs to be capitalized.

1. the librarian wanted to buy new books for the library.

2. she thought that we needed more history books for our research projects.

3. should we get more mystery stories?

4. what about biographies?

5. my teacher would like more art books.

Write three sentences about the library. Begin them with capital letters.

6. _____

_____

7. _____

_____

8. _____

_____

Beginning of a Sentence   **117**

> **Capitalize the names of the days of the week and the months of the year.**
>
> On **Monday,** Mia started swimming lessons.
> Her lessons will end in **July.**

Rewrite each sentence correctly.

1. on the last sunday in january, we took down wallpaper.

   _____

2. on the first monday in february, we painted the walls.

   _____

3. on the second wednesday in march, we installed a new carpet.

   _____

4. we put up new curtains on the third friday in april.

   _____

5. we cleaned out the cupboards on the first saturday in may.

   _____

6. last thursday, we planned our work for june.

   _____

7. when I leave for camp on the second tuesday in july, we should be done.

   _____

8. i will return from camp on the last saturday in august.

   _____

> Capitalize the names of holidays.

Martin Luther King, Jr., Day	Veterans Day
Memorial Day	Ramadan
Kwanzaa	St. Patrick's Day
Presidents' Day	Easter
Passover	Independence Day
Thanksgiving	Labor Day

Read this paragraph. Place three lines under the first letter of each word that needs to be capitalized. The first one has been done for you.

Some holidays are unique to our country. In the United States, we celebrate independence day on July 4. We also celebrate martin luther King, Jr., day and presidents' day to remember our great heroes. Although it's not unique to our country, we have bigger celebrations on St. Patrick's day than the Irish have in Ireland. In May, we remember those who died in wars on memorial day. At the end of summer, we have a long weekend because of Labor day, which honors our country's workers. On veterans day in the fall, we pay respect to those who have served in the military. On the fourth Thursday in November, families in our country have a feast on thanksgiving Day. Canadians also celebrate thanksgiving, but on a different day. All of these holidays play a part in our country's rich traditions.

Which sentence is written correctly? Fill in the bubble next to the correct answer.

1. Ⓐ we need a lot of training to get ahead.

   Ⓑ Working very hard can help us improve.

   Ⓒ no wonder some people work so hard at their goals.

   Ⓓ success depends on many things.

2. Ⓐ On the first friday of September, we will have our first game.

   Ⓑ Our last game will be on the last Saturday of october.

   Ⓒ We started practices on the third Wednesday in August.

   Ⓓ We also have practices on fridays.

3. Ⓐ Carlos's favorite holiday is Independence Day.

   Ⓑ He likes the parades on memorial Day.

   Ⓒ his second favorite holiday is Halloween.

   Ⓓ He also likes thanksgiving because of the food.

4. Ⓐ Does Rachel like to make posters?

   Ⓑ does Aidan want to enter the contest?

   Ⓒ does Maria want to paint a Thanksgiving mural?

   Ⓓ Tell mrs. carey if you would like to enter.

5. Ⓐ Kevin left on the tuesday before christmas.

   Ⓑ This year, New Year's Eve falls on a Friday.

   Ⓒ What was the forecast on groundhog day?

   Ⓓ I hope it won't be cold on st. Patrick's Day.

> ➤ Capitalize the names of people and pets.
>
> **Josh Adams** got a new cat from the pound.
>
> He named it **Buster.**
>
> **Aunt Alice** got a dog named **Hodge** from the same place.

Circle the words in each sentence that need to be capitalized.

1. Uncle joe's favorite pet was his goldfish named goldie.

2. aunt Frieda thought goldie needed company.

3. She got uncle Joe to buy a large fish called wendy.

4. Miss grace, the woman at the pet store, also showed them cats and dogs.

5. Aunt frieda and Uncle joe bought a sweet kitten.

6. Their cat fluffy never bothered uncle Joe's fish.

Write the full names of three adults whom you admire.
Remember to capitalize their names.

7. _____

8. _____

9. _____

Write the name of a pet you have, you have had, or you know.
Remember to capitalize its name.

10. _____

> **Capitalize the names of:**
>
> - specific places, such as cities, states, and parks.
>
>   Makayla visited **Philadelphia, Pennsylvania,** last year.
>   She had a great time in **Fairmount Park.**
>
> - specific things, such as the names of monuments, museums, buildings, and groups.
>
>   She saw the **Liberty Bell** with **Girl Scout Troop** 119.
>   The girls also visited the **Betsy Ross House.**

Draw three lines under the first letter of each word that needs to be capitalized.

1. Diego is going to be away from boston, Massachusetts, for a couple of days.

2. He is taking the train to new york city.

3. He wants to see the empire state building.

4. He also wants to see the metropolitan museum.

5. He loves fenway park, but he also wants to see yankee stadium.

6. Last year, Diego took a class trip to washington, D.C.

7. His favorite thing there was the washington monument.

8. He also liked the lincoln memorial.

9. Diego plans to take a day trip soon with his friends from harborview school.

10. They may visit the new england aquarium.

11. Diego went there two years ago with his boy scout troop.

12. They took pictures in front of the white house.

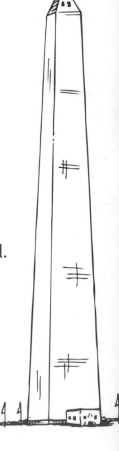

> Capitalize the first word and all other important words in the titles of movies, songs, and books.
>
> | | |
> |---|---|
> | **Movie** | <u>The Sound of Music</u> |
> | **Book** | <u>The Adventures of Huckleberry Finn</u> |
> | **Song** | "America the Beautiful" |

Circle the words that need to be capitalized in this news article.

On Friday through Sunday, members of the Springfield Community Theater will celebrate the music of George Gershwin. Gershwin's music has been used in movies like <u>An american in Paris</u> and <u>funny face</u>. Many of his songs have become famous, including "i got rhythm" and "a foggy day." The female soloist, Lita Williams, will sing "summertime" from the Gershwin show <u>Porgy and bess</u>. A local pianist, Emilio Blanco, will play "Rhapsody in blue."

Ask a friend the name of his or her favorite book. Write the title here. Remember to capitalize the important words in the title.

1. _____

List the names of your three favorite movies. Use capital letters for the first word and all other important words.

2. _____

3. _____

4. _____

Which sentence uses correct capitalization?
Fill in the bubble next to the correct answer.

1. Ⓐ Daphne left her cat snowball at home.

   Ⓑ Ima took her dog rex with her.

   Ⓒ Mrs. Guzman took her ferret Freddy for a walk.

   Ⓓ We wish we could bring our gerbil binky to school.

2. Ⓐ Alvin went with his family to kansas city.

   Ⓑ On the way, they drove through Davenport.

   Ⓒ After going to Kansas City, Alvin went to phoenix.

   Ⓓ Soon, he'll be back home in detroit.

3. Ⓐ My favorite book is <u>Charlotte's Web</u>.

   Ⓑ My favorite song is "You've got a friend."

   Ⓒ My favorite movie is <u>The parent Trap</u>.

   Ⓓ My favorite old TV show is <u>the Brady bunch</u>.

4. Ⓐ Yori flew to Chicago on new year's day.

   Ⓑ He wanted to see the sears tower.

   Ⓒ The Chicago art institute was closed.

   Ⓓ He walked all over Lincoln Park.

5. Ⓐ Did Aisha take her cat Bozo to Florida?

   Ⓑ Did she go to st. Augustine?

   Ⓒ Did she travel with the wildcats, her softball team?

   Ⓓ Did they take the plane to cape canaveral?

An abbreviation is the shortened form of a word or group of words. Some abbreviations end in a period, but many abbreviations do not.

Word or Group of Words	Abbreviation
page	p.
Avenue	Ave.
Animal Rescue League	ARL
compact disc	CD

For each word or group of words, write the letter of the correct abbreviation on the line.

1. page _____   a. CIA

2. emergency medical technician _____   b. Ave.

3. Central Intelligence Agency _____   c. p.

4. National Football League _____   d. ASAP

5. Avenue _____   e. EU

6. automated teller machine _____   f. EMT

7. as soon as possible _____   g. NFL

8. European Union _____   h. ATM

Read each group of words. Write an abbreviation for it.
Hint: These abbreviations do not end in a period.

9. American Library Association   _____

10. Public Broadcasting System   _____

Name _____

Each day of the week has an abbreviation. These abbreviations are written with a period at the end.

Day of the Week	Abbreviation
Sunday	Sun.
Monday	Mon.
Tuesday	Tue.
Wednesday	Wed.
Thursday	Thurs.
Friday	Fri.
Saturday	Sat.

Answer the following questions, using an abbreviation for one of the days of the week.

1. What is your favorite day of the week? _____

2. What is the first day of the school week? _____

3. What is the last day of the school week? _____

4. What is the first day of the weekend? _____

5. On what day or days do you exercise? _____

6. What is the second day of the school week? _____

7. What is the fourth day of the school week? _____

8. What is the day before Monday? _____

9. On what day do you have the most homework? _____

10. What day is the middle of the school week? _____

Language Fundamentals • EMC 2754 • © Evan-Moor Corp.

Most months of the year are abbreviated by using the first three letters of the name of the month, followed by a period.

Month	Abbreviation	Month	Abbreviation
January	**Jan.**	July	**July**
February	**Feb.**	August	**Aug.**
March	**Mar.**	September	**Sept.**
April	**Apr.**	October	**Oct.**
May	**May**	November	**Nov.**
June	**June**	December	**Dec.**

Use abbreviations to answer the questions about Emily's planner.

Emily's Planner			
Month	**Remember**	**Month**	**Remember**
September:	Buy school supplies	**February:**	Dad's birthday
October:	Harvest Festival	**March:**	Visit dentist
November:	Aunt Kay's for Thanksgiving	**April:**	Plant flowers
December:	Mom's birthday	**May:**	Uncle Bo's wedding
January:	Start yoga	**June:**	Vacation

1. When is the Harvest Festival? _____

2. What month will Emily go to Aunt Kay's? _____

3. When is Emily's dad's birthday? _____

4. When will Emily go to Uncle Bo's wedding? _____

5. When does school begin? _____

6. Which months do not have abbreviations? _____

> Most titles for people's names have an abbreviation.

Title	Person
Ms.	a married or unmarried woman
Mrs.	a married woman
Mr.	a married or unmarried man
Dr.	a doctor

When using a title, always use someone's last name.

Mrs. Chen   Dr. Anton

Write the correct abbreviation for the word or group of words in parentheses ( ).

1. (Doctor) Miller saw my brother yesterday. _____

2. The office manager, (a married woman's title) Wallace, schedules visits. _____

3. She had (a married or unmarried man's title) James listed on the schedule. _____

4. Everyone was surprised when (a married or unmarried woman's title) James arrived. _____

5. My teacher, (a married or unmarried woman) Oshiro, was in the waiting room. _____

6. My brother's appointment was right after (a married or unmarried man's title) Jackson's. _____

Write the names and titles of two people you know.

7. _____

8. _____

Language Fundamentals • EMC 2754 • © Evan-Moor Corp.

Name _____

Fill in the bubble next to the correct answer.

1. Which sentence contains an abbreviation?
   Ⓐ My father got a CD player for his birthday.
   Ⓑ We play music and dance.
   Ⓒ When he's not home, we play the music we like.
   Ⓓ He doesn't like some of our music.

2. Which sentence contains an abbreviation?
   Ⓐ I like dancing better than watching television.
   Ⓑ I do like watching movies on TV.
   Ⓒ It might be fun to write music for the movies.
   Ⓓ Maybe I could write theme songs for television shows.

3. Which is a correct abbreviation for one of the days of the week?
   Ⓐ Mond.
   Ⓑ tue.
   Ⓒ Wed.
   Ⓓ Thur.

4. Which is a correct abbreviation for one of the months of the year?
   Ⓐ Jan.
   Ⓑ Febr
   Ⓒ March
   Ⓓ Septem.

5. Which is a correct abbreviation for the title *doctor*?
   Ⓐ Dr
   Ⓑ Doc
   Ⓒ D.
   Ⓓ Dr.

> Most names for streets and roads have abbreviations. These abbreviations are usually written with a period at the end.

Name	Abbreviation
Road	**Rd.**
Avenue	**Ave.**
Drive	**Dr.**
Highway	**Hwy.**
Circle	**Cir.**
Boulevard	**Blvd.**
Street	**St.**
Lane	**Ln.**
Court	**Ct.**

Write the word that each underlined abbreviation stands for.

1. Suzu lives on Maple <u>St.</u>   _____

2. Her grandfather lives on Fifth <u>Ave.</u>   _____

3. To get there, Suzu's family has to drive on <u>Hwy.</u> 51.   _____

4. Suzu grew up on Coral <u>Blvd.</u>   _____

5. Her school is on Annie Oakley <u>Dr.</u>   _____

6. Suzu's best friend lives on Sunset <u>Ln.</u>   _____

Use an abbreviation for the street or road name to answer the following questions.

7. On what street do you live?   _____

8. On what street is your school?   _____

9. Name a street where a friend lives.   _____

10. Name any highway or major road in your area. _____

     Language Fundamentals • EMC 2754 • © Evan-Moor Corp.

Name _____

Each state has an abbreviation. The abbreviations for states are usually written without a period.

Alabama AL	Alaska AK	Arizona AZ	Arkansas AR	California CA
Colorado CO	Connecticut CT	Delaware DE	Florida FL	Georgia GA
Hawaii HI	Idaho ID	Illinois IL	Indiana IN	Iowa IA
Kansas KS	Kentucky KY	Louisiana LA	Maine ME	Maryland MD
Massachusetts MA	Michigan MI	Minnesota MN	Mississippi MS	Missouri MO
Montana MT	Nebraska NE	Nevada NV	New Hampshire NH	New Jersey NJ
New Mexico NM	New York NY	North Carolina NC	North Dakota ND	Ohio OH
Oklahoma OK	Oregon OR	Pennsylvania PA	Rhode Island RI	South Carolina SC
South Dakota SD	Tennessee TN	Texas TX	Utah UT	Vermont VT
Virginia VA	Washington WA	West Virginia WV	Wisconsin WI	Wyoming WY

Use state abbreviations to answer each question.

1. Which state do you live in?   _____

2. What state is close to your state?   _____

3. What state is far from your state?   _____

4. Which state would you like to visit?   _____

5. How many state abbreviations begin with *N*?   _____

6. What is the abbreviation for Arkansas?   _____

7. What is the abbreviation for Alaska?   _____

8. What is the abbreviation for Arizona?   _____

There are abbreviations for the words that measure length and weight. Some of these abbreviations are not written with a period at the end.

Length	Weight
in. = inch or inches	**oz.** = ounce or ounces
ft. = foot or feet	**lb.** = pound or pounds
cm = centimeter or centimeters	**g** = gram or grams
km = kilometer or kilometers	**kg** = kilogram or kilograms

3.5 inches = 1 mile

Use the map to answer the following questions. Use abbreviations for the units of length.

1. How far is it from the park entrance to the school? _____

2. On the map key, what unit of measurement stands for one mile? _____

3. How long is the course marked out for runners in the park? _____

4. How wide is the pond in the park? _____

Write the abbreviation for the word in parentheses ( ).

5. The package weighs one (pound). _____

6. The serving of salad dressing had four (grams) of fat. _____

7. I am 53 (inches) tall. _____

8. I am 124 (centimeters) tall. _____

Words that measure time have abbreviations. These are written with periods.

sec. = second or seconds

min. = minute or minutes

hr. = hour or hours

a.m. = before noon

p.m. = after noon

Write the correct abbreviation for each underlined word.

1. It takes 2 <u>hours</u> to get there by train.   _____

2. It took her 30 <u>seconds</u> to tie her shoe.   _____

3. Our school day is 6 <u>hours</u> and 30 <u>minutes</u> long.   _____

Use abbreviations to answer the questions.

4. What time do you wake up in the morning?   _____

5. What time do you go to sleep at night?   _____

6. How long do you take to brush your teeth?   _____

7. How long is your favorite TV show?   _____

8. The small hand on the clock points to two.
   It is dark outside. What time is it?   _____

Fill in the bubble next to the correct answer.

1. Which sentence contains an abbreviation?

   Ⓐ Anna lives in Springfield, Idaho.

   Ⓑ She has an aunt who lives on Main Avenue.

   Ⓒ Anna lives on Fourth St.

   Ⓓ Her aunt lives in the suburbs.

2. Which is the correct abbreviation for *Louisiana?*

   Ⓐ LA

   Ⓑ LO

   Ⓒ LS

   Ⓓ LI

3. Which is the correct abbreviation for *kilometer?*

   Ⓐ KR

   Ⓑ ki

   Ⓒ km

   Ⓓ kt

4. Which is the correct abbreviation for *kilogram?*

   Ⓐ ki.

   Ⓑ kil

   Ⓒ km

   Ⓓ kg

5. Which is the correct abbreviation for *ounce?*

   Ⓐ ou.

   Ⓑ oz.

   Ⓒ on.

   Ⓓ oc.

A statement ends with a period (.).

> The dog ate its dinner.

A command also usually ends with a period (.).

> Please bring me my dinner.

An exclamation ends with an exclamation point (*!*).

> The dog ate my homework!

A question ends with a question mark (*?*).

> Why is the dog so hungry?

Decide whether each of the following sentences has the correct or incorrect end mark. Circle the answer you choose.

1. Do you know the way to San Jose.   correct   incorrect

2. Zachary has an uncle there.   correct   incorrect

3. He has a huge house!   correct   incorrect

4. Please hand me the map.   correct   incorrect

Write the end punctuation mark for each of the following sentences.

5. Did you see today's game_____

6. I can't believe we won_____

7. We worked on catching the ball today_____

8. Please wash my uniform_____

> Be sure to use the correct end mark when writing a sentence.
>
> A statement or command ends with a period (.).
>
> We play sports at our school.
> Please hand me that bat.
>
> A question ends with a question mark (?).
>
> Which sport is your favorite?
>
> An exclamation ends with an exclamation point (!).
>
> I love baseball!

Write the correct end mark for each sentence.

1. Was the volleyball game yesterday_____

2. Oh no, we lost the game_____

3. I plan to play volleyball next year_____

Add end marks to the sentences in the following paragraph.

Why do you think many schools have classes in Physical Education_____ Students need to exercise their large muscles_____ What kind of activities are in P.E. class_____ At many schools, students can learn basic rules and skills for games like basketball, volleyball, and soccer_____ Students might also learn how to square dance and do basic gymnastics_____ There's something really fun for everyone_____ Do you want to get some exercise_____ Sign up for a school sport today_____

     Language Fundamentals • EMC 2754 • © Evan-Moor Corp.

Which sentence has the correct end punctuation?
Fill in the bubble next to the correct answer.

1. Ⓐ Are music lessons good for students.
   Ⓑ Lusita takes guitar lessons.
   Ⓒ She says that guitar lessons are great?
   Ⓓ Lusita really likes her lessons

2. Ⓐ Which do you like better, piano or guitar!
   Ⓑ Bao takes piano lessons!
   Ⓒ Piano lessons are terrific!
   Ⓓ Bao's father is glad Bao is getting lessons!

3. Ⓐ Do you like all kinds of music?
   Ⓑ Kaitlyn likes playing pop songs?
   Ⓒ She says, "They rock?"
   Ⓓ Kaitlyn also likes classical music

4. Ⓐ Ms. Desai teaches music at school.
   Ⓑ She says it's really fun?
   Ⓒ I want to teach music when I grow up
   Ⓓ Ms. Desai told me to work hard?

5. Ⓐ Drums are my favorite instrument
   Ⓑ Ms. Mack plays drums
   Ⓒ Do you like drums, too.
   Ⓓ They're really loud!

Name _____

> Use commas to separate three or more words or group of words in a series.
>
> My favorite pets are **dogs, cats, and birds.**
>
> We went to the **pet store, the grocery store, and the department store.**

Circle *correct* or *incorrect* to show whether commas are used correctly in the following sentences.

1. My cat likes to run, jump meow, and play.   correct   incorrect

2. My dog likes to eat, run, bark, and play.   correct   incorrect

3. I took my cat to the vet to the store, and to my house.   correct   incorrect

4. I took my dog to the vet, to the store, and to the park.   correct   incorrect

5. My cat likes to eat tuna, and chicken.   correct   incorrect

6. My dog likes to eat beef, chicken, and pork.   correct   incorrect

Write each sentence correctly, placing commas where they are needed.

7. Matt has a rabbit a parrot and a dog.

_____

8. Stephanie wants to go to the animal shelter adopt a pet and bring it home.

_____

_____

Language Fundamentals • EMC 2754 • © Evan-Moor Corp.

> Use commas to separate three or more words or group of words in a series.
>
> Jasmine has to do **writing, reading, and math** before bedtime.
>
> Dylan needs to **wash the dishes, take out the trash, and do his homework** before bedtime.

Add commas where they belong in each series.

1. I studied last night with Leah Bryan and Sean.

2. We worked on math reading and spelling.

3. Afterwards, I watched TV ate dessert and went to bed.

4. This morning, I got up got dressed and went to school.

5. I have a peanut butter sandwich a box of raisins and a bag of carrots for lunch.

6. After school, do you want to stay home go to the park or go to Eric's house?

7. If you stay home, will you do chores do your homework or play video games?

8. For dinner, I had fish rice green beans and salad.

9. Before bed, I took a bath brushed my teeth and read a book.

Write a sentence about what you did last night. Use three or more words or groups of words in a series. Remember to place commas where they belong.

10. _____

_____

_____

Compound sentences use words such as *and*, *but*, or *or* to join two simple sentences. Place a comma before the joining word in a compound sentence.

We're going out to dinner, **and** we're going to a movie after that.
Julio wants to eat at a Chinese restaurant, **but** I want to eat at a French cafe.
Teresa might stay home, **or** she might go with us.

In each compound sentence, insert a comma where it belongs.

1. Mia wanted to go on the field trip but she was sick that day.

2. We went to a huge dairy farm and we ate delicious ice cream afterwards.

3. Last year we went to a museum but this year we wanted to do something different.

4. We were supposed to be on our best behavior but some children were noisy.

5. Do you think they were excited or do you think they were just being mischievous?

6. It was good to be outdoors this year and our class really enjoyed the trip.

Write your own compound sentence about a special school activity.
Remember to use a comma.

7. _____

_____

_____

Write your own compound sentence about a trip you took.
Remember to use a comma.

8. _____

_____

_____

A complex sentence uses words such as *although, because, when, since,* and *while* to join two related sentences. If the joining word comes at the beginning of the sentence, use a comma between the two sentences.

Although I liked the gift, I thought my aunt spent too much money on it.

For each sentence, insert a comma if one is needed.

1. Although I am younger than my sister I am older than my brother Max.

2. Because I am older than Max he wants to be like me.

3. When he gets to be my age he'll probably feel different about it.

4. While Max looks up to me I look up to my sister Jessica.

5. Although it might not mean much to her I like to go to all of her softball games.

6. Since she's the oldest Jessica is our role model.

Write two complex sentences about the members of your family. Start your sentences with *although, while, when,* or *because.* Remember to use a comma to separate the two sentences when you join them.

7. _____

_____

_____

8. _____

_____

_____

Which sentence is written correctly?
Fill in the bubble next to the correct answer.

1. Ⓐ The room was crowded with chairs sofas and tables.
   Ⓑ We sold dishes old clothes and furniture at our garage sale.
   Ⓒ My brother my sister and my mother all worked hard.
   Ⓓ Neighbors, strangers, and friends all came to the sale.

2. Ⓐ Kevin walked to the bus stop got on the bus and got off at school.
   Ⓑ He went to his first class, went to his second class, and then went to P.E.
   Ⓒ In P.E., he practiced running dribbling a ball and passing.
   Ⓓ After P.E., he went to math class then social studies and then the lunchroom.

3. Ⓐ Sonia tried out for the school play, and she got the biggest part.
   Ⓑ She is really good at acting but it's hard to hear her voice.
   Ⓒ Will people enjoy the show or will they be bored?
   Ⓓ Sonia has been practicing speaking loudly, and, she's much easier to hear.

4. Ⓐ Although Ahmed likes science he likes art best of all.
   Ⓑ While, some enjoy painting still life, he prefers painting portraits.
   Ⓒ Although he is young, his artwork is very advanced.
   Ⓓ While no one else was surprised Ahmed was amazed when he won the contest.

5. Ⓐ Although Serena loves theater she is really best at writing.
   Ⓑ When everyone read her story they recognized her talent.
   Ⓒ While Serena works at writing, her sister works at acting.
   Ⓓ When they grow up they may choose other careers.

> Use a comma between the day and the year in a date.
>
> July 4, 1865
>
> February 18, 2010

Rewrite each sentence. Add commas where they are needed.

1. My sister was born on November 12 2006.

   _____

2. My mother and father got married on June 18 1996.

   _____

3. We are having a party for my grandmother on September 14 2008.

   _____

   _____

4. She turns 65 on September 10 2008.

   _____

5. I met my best friend on September 1 2005.

   _____

6. She was born on June 9 2000.

   _____

> Use a comma to separate the year in a date from the part of the sentence that follows it.
>
> On September 14, 1977, the city opened the new youth center.
>
> On September 14, 2007, the youth center turned 30.

Add commas where they are needed in the following sentences.

1. On August 26 1920 women gained the right to vote in the United States.

2. On November 19, 1863 President Lincoln gave the Gettysburg Address.

3. On January 20 1992 Maya Angelou read her poem at the Presidential Inauguration.

4. On May 5 2006 we celebrated Cinco de Mayo.

5. On November 22, 1963 Lyndon Johnson became president of the United States.

6. On July 4 1776 the Continental Congress approved the Declaration of Independence.

7. On January 20, 1892 the first official basketball game was played.

8. On October 27, 2004 the Boston Red Sox won the World Series.

Complete the sentences. Use commas correctly.

9. I was born on _____ in the state of _____.
   (month, day, year)

10. _____ was an important day in my life because
    (month, day, year)

    _____.

Name _____

> When writing someone's address on an envelope, use a comma between the name of the city and the state abbreviation.
>
> Madison Lincoln   Melissa Hampton
> 1010 Fifth Street   222 Bellvista Road
> Albany, NY 12203   St. Louis, MO 63108

Add commas where they are needed to the addresses below.

1. Ben MacMillan
   34 Pinetree Lane
   Concord NH 03201

2. Yolanda Williams
   17 Central Street
   New Haven CT 06610

3. Ms. Patty Street
   42 Mandolin Lane
   Orlando FL 32205

4. Laura Sanchez
   4070 Main Street
   Cleveland OH 44202

5. Mr. Mark Lieu
   3820 28th Street
   San Francisco CA 94431

6. Roberto Carmina
   14820 Atlantic Avenue
   Leonia NJ 07205

Write your address below. Remember to use a comma where it belongs.

_____

_____

_____

Use a comma to separate the name of a city from the name of a state, province, or country.

> The temperature was hot in Phoenix, Arizona.

Use a comma to separate the name of a state, province, or country from the part of the sentence that follows it.

> The temperature in Montreal, Quebec, was really cold.
>
> In Paris, France, the weather was rainy.

Add commas where they belong.

1. In Detroit Michigan many cars are made.

2. In Gettysburg Pennsylvania many apples are grown.

3. There are great jobs in Dublin Ireland for people who live there.

4. When I went to Savannah Georgia I saw peach trees.

5. In Sydney Australia there is a great opera house.

6. We went to San Diego California on spring break.

7. In Toronto Ontario we went to a film festival.

8. The Olympics in Salt Lake City Utah were very exciting.

9. In Austin Texas we heard fantastic music.

10. I want to go to Cairo Egypt someday.

Use a comma after the greeting in a friendly letter.

> Dear Aunt Margaret,
>
> Dear Lupe,

Use a comma after the closing in any letter.

> Sincerely,
>
> Love,

Read these letters. Insert commas where they belong.

Dear Mom

You were right. Summer camp is really fun!

Love
Kim

Dear Ms. Lawson

Thank you for looking after Snuffles while we were gone. That was very nice of you.

Sincerely
Janie Lampert

Dear Paris

Thanks for the tickets. The show was awesome!

Your cousin
Frankie

Dear Grandma

I can't wait to see you next summer! I hope we can go swimming together again.

Love
Zoe

> Use a comma to separate the name of the person being addressed from the rest of the sentence.
>
> Lucia, where did you get those roller skates?
> What are you doing tonight, Max?

Write these sentences correctly by adding commas where they are needed.

1. Jacob would you please grab the paintbrush?

   _____

2. Is it time for your lesson Haley?

   _____

3. Mom I want a birthday party, please.

   _____

4. Ms. Iyo I won't be in school tomorrow.

   _____

5. Auntie Roseann would you sign this form for our field trip?

   _____

   _____

6. What was it like when you were in fourth grade Grandpa?

   _____

   _____

   Language Fundamentals • EMC 2754 • © Evan-Moor Corp.

Name _____

Fill in the bubble next to the correct answer.

1. Which sentence is written correctly?

   Ⓐ Mrs. Gallagher's son was born on May 7, 2004.

   Ⓑ Her daughter was born on October 15 2006.

   Ⓒ Mrs. Gallagher was born on November, 27 1980.

   Ⓓ On September 2 1985 she started kindergarten.

2. Which sentence is written correctly?

   Ⓐ On September 10, 2005 the school celebrated its 50th anniversary.

   Ⓑ On September 10, 1955, the school was a very different place.

   Ⓒ By September 12 1980 the number of students had doubled.

   Ⓓ On October 5 2005, we will hold a reunion.

3. Which sentence is written correctly?

   Ⓐ In Alexandria, Virginia, there are many historical places to visit.

   Ⓑ When we went to Seattle Washington we saw Pioneer Square.

   Ⓒ In Portland, Oregon we went to coffee houses.

   Ⓓ In St. Paul Minnesota we went to the symphony.

4. Which greeting for a friendly letter is written correctly?

   Ⓐ Dear Jackson

   Ⓑ Dear, Mackenzie

   Ⓒ Dear Alejandro:

   Ⓓ Dear Molly,

5. Which sentence is written correctly?

   Ⓐ Can I borrow your pink sweater Erin?

   Ⓑ Paige I think, you lost that sweater.

   Ⓒ Erin, you must have something else I can wear.

   Ⓓ Paige I really don't think that I do.

Use commas to separate quotations—the exact words someone says—from the rest of the sentence.

If the comma comes after the quotation, place the comma before the ending quotation mark.

Hunter said, "I have to sell some wrapping paper for the school fundraiser."

"I'll buy three rolls," Hunter's aunt replied.

These sentences contain dialogue. Add commas where they belong.

1. Maria asked "What club do you want to join?"

2. "I want to join the chess club" Melanie said.

3. "I don't know how to play chess" Ian said.

4. "We could join the reading group" Melanie said.

5. Maria said "I'm not sure."

6. "I am" Ian replied.

7. "I'd like to be on a sports team" Koji said.

8. Maria said "I'd really love to be in the choir."

9. "I would, too" Ian answered.

10. "I guess we'll do different things" Koji said.

11. "That's okay" said Maria.

12. "We will see each other in class" agreed Ian.

> Use quotation marks to separate the exact words someone says.
>
> "We went straight from winter to summer this year," said Olivia.
> Soon Li replied, "That is putting it mildly!"

Rewrite each sentence, placing quotation marks where they belong.

1. Ava said, My little brother and I went to the dentist today.

   _____

2. Floss your teeth, said Dr. Smith.

   _____

3. The dentist gave me floss, said Ava.

   _____

4. Ava said, The dentist told me I was a good sport.

   _____

Rewrite each sentence correctly.

5. It's great to be able to speak more than one language said Mason.

   _____

   _____

6. Luis replied I speak English and Spanish.

   _____

> If a quotation is interrupted by words telling who is speaking, use quotation marks to set off the speaker's exact words.
>
> "It's hot in here," said Elijah, "and I'll be happy to get outside."

Rewrite each sentence correctly. Remember to use quotation marks.

1. I like to eat pizza, said Ethan, but not every day.

_____

_____

2. I'd rather eat pasta, said Ashley, as long as there are meatballs.

_____

_____

3. If I could cook, said Juan, I'd eat steak every day.

_____

_____

4. My mother says if I learn to cook, said Ashley, I might stop being so picky.

_____

_____

5. I want to be a great cook someday, said Ethan, so I can eat just what I want.

_____

_____

> Use quotation marks around the titles of short stories, poems, and songs.
>
> "Apple Blossoms"   "Jellyfish Stew"   "Rosalita"

Write each of the following titles correctly. Remember to use quotation marks.

1. *(short story)* How the Alphabet Was Made

   _____

2. *(poem)* The Raven

   _____

3. *(song)* This Land Is Your Land

   _____

Write an answer to each question. Remember to use quotation marks correctly.

4. What is your favorite song?

   _____

5. What is your favorite short story?

   _____

6. What is your favorite poem?

   _____

Underline the titles of books, movies, television shows, newspapers, and magazines.

<u>The Trumpet of the Swan</u>
<u>Aladdin</u>
<u>Lizzie Maguire</u>
<u>The Sacramento Bee</u>
<u>Highlights for Children</u>

If you are using a computer, use *italics* for titles.

The Trumpet of the Swan by E. B. White   *Highlights for Children*

Correct the following paragraph. Remember to underline the titles of movies, books, newspapers, magazines, and television shows.

My favorite movie is Nanny McPhee. I read an article about it in the Springfield Times and couldn't wait to see it. Then I read more about it in Newsweek. I thought Emma Thompson was fantastic playing the part of the nanny. That made me curious about what else she had done. I looked to see if she was ever on television. Funnily enough, she played a children's entertainer on the old TV show Cheers, and her character's name was Nanny G. I thought that Emma Thompson was terrific in this movie!

Answer the question with a complete sentence.

What book are you reading now?

_____

_____

Fill in the bubble next to the correct answer.

1. Which sentence is written correctly?

   Ⓐ Mrs. Gomez said "I think it's time to go home.

   Ⓑ Her daughter said, "I don't want to go."

   Ⓒ Mrs. Gomez, said, "We're all getting hungry."

   Ⓓ That's true said her daughter.

2. Which sentence is written correctly?

   Ⓐ Alexis told me that "spring is her favorite season."

   Ⓑ Jose said, "I prefer summer."

   Ⓒ Julia said "I like winter."

   Ⓓ Kyle said, I like fall.

3. Which sentence is written correctly?

   Ⓐ "I can't decide, said Morgan "what I want to be when I grow up."

   Ⓑ "The problem is," said Jackson, you have too many choices."

   Ⓒ "I think," said Morgan, "that you may be right."

   Ⓓ Of course, said Jackson, I'm always right.

4. Which short story title is written correctly?

   Ⓐ The Brief Adventures of a Small Mouse

   Ⓑ *The Brief Adventures of a Small Mouse*

   Ⓒ The Brief Adventures of a Small Mouse

   Ⓓ "The Brief Adventures of a Small Mouse"

5. Which book title is written correctly?

   Ⓐ The Beastly Feast

   Ⓑ "The Beastly Feast"

   Ⓒ *The Beastly Feast*

   Ⓓ The Beastly "Feast"

A contraction is a shortened form of two words. Use an apostrophe (')
in place of any missing letter or letters.

could not	couldn't	do not	don't
will not	won't	she would	she'd
they are	they're	I will	I'll
we have	we've	let us	let's
he is	he's		

Match each set of two words to the correct contraction.

1. is not   ●

2. we will   ●

3. would not ●

4. she is   ●

5. are not   ●

6. they have ●

● aren't

● she's

● isn't

● they've

● we'll

● wouldn't

Write the two words that form each contraction.

7. shouldn't _____

8. won't _____

9. they're _____

10. they'll _____

11. she'd _____

12. he's _____

Language Fundamentals • EMC 2754 • © Evan-Moor Corp.

> Add an apostrophe (') and *s* to a singular noun to make it possessive.
>
> Bella's hat
>
> Luis's microscope
>
> the dog's tail

Rewrite the following sentences. Add an apostrophe (') and an *s* to correct the possessive nouns.

1. The dentist cleaned the little <u>girl</u> teeth.

   _____

2. <u>Charles</u> breakfast was delicious.

   _____

3. The <u>man</u> tie was on crooked.

   _____

4. <u>Alyssa</u> bus was late.

   _____

5. The <u>child</u> school was closed.

   _____

6. The <u>principal</u> car had snow tires.

   _____

> If a plural noun ends in *s*, just add an apostrophe (') to make it possessive.
>
> the brothers' mistakes
>
> the sisters' room
>
> the cats' collars
>
> If a plural noun does not end with an *s*, add an apostrophe (') and an *s* to make it possessive.
>
> the children's party
>
> the women's meeting

Rewrite each sentence. Use the correct possessive form for the underlined plural nouns.

1. This is the <u>teachers</u> lounge.

   _____

2. These are the <u>girls</u> bicycles.

   _____

3. The <u>boys</u> jackets are hung in the coat room.

   _____

4. The <u>animals</u> cages need to be cleaned.

   _____

5. The <u>students</u> chores are listed on the board.

   _____

6. The <u>mens</u> restroom was closed for cleaning.

   _____

> Use a colon to separate the hour from the minutes to write the time.

three hours and twenty-four minutes	**3:24**
six o'clock	**6:00**
eight thirty	**8:30**
a quarter past seven	**7:15**

Write the times listed below, using numerals and colons.

1. six thirty   _____

2. two hours and fourteen minutes   _____

3. one hour and twenty-eight minutes   _____

4. twelve o'clock   _____

5. four hours and forty-seven minutes   _____

6. seven thirty   _____

7. nine fifty   _____

8. a quarter past ten   _____

9. eleven o'clock   _____

10. 15 minutes after three   _____

> In a friendly letter, use a comma after the greeting.
>
> Dear Jeanie,
>
> In a business letter, use a colon after the greeting.
>
> To Whom It May Concern:
>
> Dear Officer Okamora:
>
> Dear Sir or Madam:

Read the greetings below. Circle whether the greetings are for a business or friendly letter.

1. Dear Tej,	business	friendly
2. Dear Professor Jones:	business	friendly
3. Dear Senator Garcia:	business	friendly
4. Dear Grandpa,	business	friendly
5. To Whom It May Concern:	business	friendly

Write the beginning of a business letter to your principal. Write the opening sentence for your letter, stating the reason you are writing. Remember to use a colon after the greeting.

Greeting: _____

Opening Sentence: _____

_____

_____

_____

Name _____

Fill in the bubble next to the correct answer.

1. Which contraction is written correctly?

   Ⓐ dont

   Ⓑ shes'

   Ⓒ theyll

   Ⓓ didn't

2. Which singular possessive is written correctly?

   Ⓐ Josés house

   Ⓑ Shawnas' toy

   Ⓒ Jason's journey

   Ⓓ Colins book

3. Which plural possessive is written correctly?

   Ⓐ the dogs breakfast

   Ⓑ the children's workshop

   Ⓒ the ladies purses

   Ⓓ the cats's purring

4. Which time is written correctly?

   Ⓐ 1015

   Ⓑ 10:15

   Ⓒ 10:fifteen

   Ⓓ ten 15

5. Which greeting is written correctly for a business letter?

   Ⓐ Dear John,

   Ⓑ Dear Sir

   Ⓒ Dear Mr. Bailey

   Ⓓ Dear Mr. Bailey:

Articles are words that introduce nouns. The words *a*, *an*, and *the* are articles.

- Use *a* before a word that begins with a consonant sound.

- Use *an* before a word that begins with a vowel or a vowel sound.

Cal kicked **the** ball through **an** opening in **a** wall **an** hour ago.

Circle each article. Underline the noun it introduces.

1. Sook Hee carried an umbrella and wore boots.

2. Cal wore a huge sweatshirt.

3. Sook Hee's umbrella had a big flower on top.

4. Cal's sweatshirt had an orange tiger on it.

5. Sook Hee brought a yellow umbrella for Cal.

Write *a* or *an* in each blank.

6. Cal dropped _____ glove in a puddle.

7. Yoon Ki used _____ long stick to get the glove out of the puddle.

8. Cal made _____ enormous splash with his boots.

9. Yoon Ki made _____ smaller splash with her umbrella.

10. Cal ate _____ egg sandwich for lunch.

11. Yoon Ki had _____ apple and cheese crackers.

12. The friends shared _____ chocolate cupcake for dessert.

The words *a* and *an* are called indefinite articles. Use them to refer to any person, animal, place, or thing.

Dad bought me **a** video game and **an** ice-cream cone.

The word *the* is called a definite article. Use it to refer to a specific person, animal, place, or thing.

The video game was hard to play, but **the** ice cream was delicious!

Underline the article. Then circle *definite* or *indefinite* to show the kind of article that is underlined.

1. We saw a display of computers in one store.	definite	indefinite
2. The computer I wanted was too expensive.	definite	indefinite
3. Dad took me to an old store downtown.	definite	indefinite
4. They had the same computer!	definite	indefinite
5. Dad bought it and a video game for himself.	definite	indefinite

Write the correct article in each blank.

6. My sister wanted _____ new CD player.

7. Mom took her to _____ store nearest our house.

8. They looked in _____ enormous room full of CD players.

9. My sister didn't like _____ CD players at that store.

10. She found _____ one she wanted at a different store.

When there are two negatives in the same sentence, it's called a double negative. Avoid using double negatives.

no   not   never   none   nothing   nobody   nowhere   hardly   barely

Incorrect   My sister does **not** like **no** old CDs.

Correct   My sister does **not** like old CDs.

Rewrite each sentence to have only one negative.

1. Jake never misses no ballgame.

   _____

2. He does not cheer for no visiting team.

   _____

Using words from the word box, write sentences using negatives.
Avoid using double negatives.

> no   not   none   never   nothing   nobody

3. _____

   _____

4. _____

   _____ .

5. _____

   _____

   Language Fundamentals • EMC 2754 • © Evan-Moor Corp.

> It is easy to confuse words such as *good*, *well*, *bad*, and *badly*.
>
> - *Good* is an adjective. Use *good* to describe nouns.
> - *Well* is usually an adverb. Use *well* to describe action verbs.
>
>   Irma plays the piano **well.** She is a **good** pianist.
>
> - *Bad* is an adjective. Use *bad* to describe nouns.
> - *Badly* is an adverb. Use *badly* to describe action verbs.
>
>   Kasey sings very **badly.** She is a **bad** singer.

Write *good* or *well* to describe each underlined word.

1. Pam makes _____ pasta <u>sauce</u>.

2. She uses _____ <u>tomatoes</u> and <u>onions</u>.

3. She <u>stirs</u> the mixture _____ as it cooks.

4. Dad told Pam that she <u>did</u> very _____.

5. Mom says that no one makes pasta <u>sauce</u> as _____ as Pam's.

Write *bad* or *badly* to describe each underlined word.

6. Jiro <u>skates</u> very _____.

7. He makes very _____ <u>spins</u>.

8. He <u>jumps</u> _____, too.

9. He wears a _____ <u>costume</u>.

10. He <u>performs</u> _____ at every contest.

Fill in the bubble next to the correct answer.

1. Choose the article that belongs in the blank.
   Be sure to take _____ umbrella when it's raining.

   Ⓐ a

   Ⓑ an

   Ⓒ am

   Ⓓ and

2. Choose the definite article.

   Ⓐ a

   Ⓑ an

   Ⓒ the

   Ⓓ some

3. Which sentence is written correctly?

   Ⓐ No one can't beat me at chess.

   Ⓑ Randy never makes no home runs.

   Ⓒ Neka never brings an apple in her lunch.

   Ⓓ Our teacher doesn't give us no homework on Fridays.

4. Which sentence is written correctly?

   Ⓐ Mom puts nothing on her toast.

   Ⓑ Mom never puts nothing on her toast.

   Ⓒ Mom does not put nothing on her toast.

   Ⓓ Mom does not never put anything on her toast.

5. Which sentence is written correctly?

   Ⓐ Liz kicks very good.

   Ⓑ Liz plays hockey well.

   Ⓒ Liz plays a well game.

   Ⓓ Liz can pass the ball good.

> Some words are easily confused because they sound alike but are spelled differently. Use the correct spelling for each meaning.
>
> - Use *they're* as a contraction for *they are.*
>   **They're** wearing warm boots today.
>
> - Use *there* to point out a place.
>   Please leave your boots over **there.**
>
> - Use *their* to show ownership.
>   They clean **their** boots well.
>
> - Use *you're* as a contraction for *you are.*
>   **You're** studying for a test.
>
> - Use *your* to show ownership.
>   You are proud of **your** good grades.

Draw lines to match each phrase with its meaning.

1. belongs to them •   • your

2. a place   •   • their

3. you are   •   • they're

4. belongs to you   •   • there

5. they are   •   • you're

Write the correct word from the rule box in each sentence.

6. Kat and Lam gave _____ report first.

7. You gave _____ report second.

8. Everyone says that _____ a good student.

9. Everyone tells Lita and Jack that _____ good students.

10. Tito and Amanda go to the library and study _____.

Some words are easy to confuse because the spelling is so similar. Be sure to use the correct spelling for the word's meaning.

- Use *it's* as a contraction for *it is.*
    It's fun to play with a dog.

- Use *its* to show ownership.
    I saw a dog wagging **its** tail.

- Use *we're* as a contraction for *we are.*
    We're trying to find a puppy to adopt.

- Use *were* to show the past tense of *are.*
    The puppies at the shelter **were** so cute!

- Use *where* when talking about a place.
    We have a good place **where** a puppy can sleep.

Draw a line to match each word with its meaning.

1. were •   • we are

2. its •   • past tense of *are*

3. where •   • belongs to it

4. we're •   • it is

5. it's •   • a place

Circle the correct word to complete the sentence.

6. My parents and I (were, where, we're) looking for a puppy to adopt.

7. We chose this puppy because we love (it's, its) long, soft ears.

8. We made a bed (were, where, we're) it can sleep.

9. I think the puppy is so cute when (its, it's) sleeping.

10. (Were, Where, We're) happy to have the puppy!

Which word correctly completes the sentence?
Fill in the bubble next to the correct answer.

1. *My brothers put on _____ bathing suits.*

Ⓐ they

Ⓑ there

Ⓒ their

Ⓓ they're

2. *_____ going to the water park today.*

Ⓐ They

Ⓑ There

Ⓒ Their

Ⓓ They're

3. *My brother's friends will meet them _____.*

Ⓐ they

Ⓑ there

Ⓒ their

Ⓓ they're

4. *_____ fun to go to the water park.*

Ⓐ Is

Ⓑ It

Ⓒ Its

Ⓓ It's

5. *The park opens _____ gates at 8 o'clock.*

Ⓐ is

Ⓑ it

Ⓒ its

Ⓓ it's

> A base word is the main word part before a prefix or a suffix is added.

prefix	+	base word	=	new word
re		**use**		reuse

base word	+	suffix	=	new word
use		ful		useful

Circle each prefix or suffix. Write the base word on the line.

1. harmful   harmless   _____

2. breakable   rebreak   _____

3. kindly   kindness   _____

4. sharpen   sharpener   _____

5. careful   careless   _____

6. remind   mindful   _____

Circle the base word in each underlined word.

Carlo has an <u>agreement</u> with his friend. They go to the skating rink

<u>weekly</u>. They work hard to become better <u>skaters</u>. They practice their

<u>imperfect</u> moves over and over. They spin <u>quickly</u> and jump <u>carefully</u>.

Soon their <u>performances</u> are perfect.

Name _____

A prefix is a word part added at the beginning of a word.

The prefix *un–* means "not" or "the opposite of."

un + happy = unhappy = not happy

un + cover = uncover = the opposite of *cover*

Find and circle eight words that have the prefix *un–*.

```
a  u  r  u  x  j  p  n  w  y  u  p
g  n  n  u  n  a  b  l  e  n  o
m  h  e  l  s  e  a  t  y  i  h  y
i  a  e  o  i  a  d  u  a  w  o  b
e  p  e  c  u  k  l  n  n  d  o  d
f  p  r  k  t  e  e  d  h  m  k  c
c  y  r  e  u  n  c  o  v  e  r  s
k  e  e  u  n  z  i  p  p  t  a  l
r  t  e  u  n  j  b  x  p  q  s  a
```

Write the base words of the words you circled.

_____   _____   _____   _____

_____   _____   _____   _____

Adding a prefix changes the meaning of the base word.

Dis– means "not" or "the opposite of."

> **dis**like = not like
> **dis**appear = the opposite of appear
> **dis**respect = not respect

Pre– means "before."

> **pre**read = read before
> **pre**view = view before
> **pre**cut = cut before

Re– means "again."

> **re**read = read again
> **re**view = view again
> **re**tell = tell again

Read each clue. Write the words in the puzzle.

Across
2. not able
5. not continue
6. do again
7. wrap before

Down
1. view before
2. not honest
3. opposite of *prove*
4. read again

Language Fundamentals • EMC 2754 • © Evan-Moor Corp.

The suffix *–less* means "without."

hope + less = hope**less** = without hope

care + less = care**less** = without care

Find and circle the ten words that have the suffix *–less.*

```
c  u  r  p  s  s  i  g  h  t  l  e  s  s
g  a  n  g  r  a  c  e  l  e  s  s  a  i
m  h  r  l  s  i  h  e  l  p  l  e  s  s
i  a  e  e  i  a  c  u  a  w  o  b  j  g
e  p  g  e  l  x  j  e  n  s  o  d  o  k
h  a  r  m  l  e  s  s  l  m  k  c  b  t
h  o  p  e  l  e  s  s  v  e  r  s  q  h
c  l  u  e  l  e  s  s  p  t  s  l  d  m
r  t  h  o  u  g  h  t  l  e  s  s  s  e
f  l  p  n  r  s  e  n  s  e  l  e  s  s
```

Write the base words of the words you circled.

_____ _____ _____ _____ _____

_____ _____ _____ _____ _____

Use one of the words you circled in a sentence.

_____

_____

Adding a suffix changes the meaning of the base word.

- *–ful* means "full of"
  hope**ful** = full of hope
- *–less* means "without"
  hope**less** = without hope
- *–able* means "the ability to be"
  break**able** = can be broken
- *–ward* means "in the direction of"
  back**ward** = toward the back

Read each clue. Write the words in the puzzle.

Across
4. full of harm
6. full of hope
8. without fear

Down
1. has the ability to be washed
2. full of care
3. in a down direction
5. without skin
7. in an up direction

Add suffixes to some verbs and adjectives to make them into nouns.

teach + **er** = teacher

He is a good **teacher**.

act + **or** = actor

He is a well-known **actor**.

kind + **ness** = kindness

Everyone knew of his **kindness**.

treat + **ment** = treatment

He appreciates her **treatment**.

Form a noun by adding a suffix to each word.

ness   ment   or   er

1. sail _____

2. paint _____

3. glad _____

4. agree _____

5. sweet _____

Use words that you made above to complete these sentences.

6. The _____ painted a beautiful picture.

7. The picture showed his feelings of joy and _____.

8. Everyone talked about the _____ of the children's faces.

Fill in the bubble next to the correct answer.

1. What is the base word in *recharge?*

   Ⓐ re

   Ⓑ char

   Ⓒ charge

   Ⓓ rec

2. What is the prefix in *unhelpfully?*

   Ⓐ un

   Ⓑ help

   Ⓒ ful

   Ⓓ ly

3. Which word means "appear again"?

   Ⓐ reappear

   Ⓑ disappear

   Ⓒ preappear

   Ⓓ appeared

4. What is the suffix in *unsinkable?*

   Ⓐ un

   Ⓑ sink

   Ⓒ sinkable

   Ⓓ able

5. Which word means "without hope"?

   Ⓐ hoping

   Ⓑ hopeful

   Ⓒ hopeless

   Ⓓ hopefulness

A contraction is a word formed from two words by leaving out some letters. Use an apostrophe in the place of any missing letter or letters.

These words are contractions made with the word *not*:

ca**n't** ⟶ can not		are**n't** ⟶ are not	
have**n't** ⟶ have not		did**n't** ⟶ did not	
were**n't** ⟶ were not		could**n't** ⟶ could not	

Write the contraction made from each pair of words. Circle the letter that the apostrophe replaces.

1. is + not =   _____

2. do + not =   _____

3. was + not =   _____

4. had + not =   _____

5. have + not =   _____

6. does + not =   _____

7. should + not = _____

Complete each sentence with a contraction formed by *not* and the word in parentheses.

8. Maria was so tired that she _____ finish her homework.
                                              (could)

9. Mr. Lopez said, "You _____ have to finish today."
                                    (do)

10. Because of Mr. Lopez's kindness, Maria's homework _____ late.
                                                                      (was)

> Many contractions are made with forms of the verb *to be.*
>
> I am ⟶ **I'm**   we are ⟶ **we're**
>
> she is ⟶ **she's**   they are ⟶ **they're**
>
> it is ⟶ **it's**   you are ⟶ **you're**

Complete the chart. The first one has been done for you.

Two Words	Contraction	What Apostrophe Replaces
1. he is	he's	i
2. you are		
3. they are		
4. it is		
5. I am		
6. we are		

Write a contraction with a form of *to be* to complete each sentence.

7. The rain has stopped, and _____ sunny outside.

8. The friends have decided that _____ going to go to the beach.

9. Marlo and I agreed that _____ going to the zoo Saturday.

10. When we got there, I said to Marlo, "_____ happy to see all the animals."

Fill in the bubble next to the correct answer.

1. Which contraction is made from *could not*?

   (A) can't

   (B) cannot

   (C) couldn't

   (D) shouldn't

2. Which contraction is made from *it is*?

   (A) it's

   (B) I'm

   (C) isn't

   (D) hasn't

3. Which word correctly completes the sentence?
   The twins bought sleeping bags because _____ going camping.

   (A) he's

   (B) it's

   (C) you're

   (D) they're

4. Which word correctly completes the sentence?
   I love baseball, so _____ going to the game today.

   (A) I'm

   (B) It's

   (C) I've

   (D) Isn't

5. Which word correctly completes the sentence?
   We _____ seen any new movies lately.

   (A) can't

   (B) haven't

   (C) aren't

   (D) hasn't

Synonyms are words that mean almost the same thing.

happy = glad   *scared = frightened*
I'm **happy** it's summer.   Lucas was **scared** to go on the ride.
Sarita's **glad,** too.   Ted was **frightened,** too.

Write a synonym for each word.

rough   foolish   wealthy   similar   exhausted   furious

1. alike _____

2. rich _____

3. silly _____

4. angry _____

5. bumpy _____

6. tired _____

Pick two pairs of synonyms from the exercise above. Write four sentences.

7. _____

_____

8. _____

_____

9. _____

_____

10. _____

_____

> Use synonyms to vary your writing and to make it more descriptive and interesting.
>
> Synonyms for *good:* fine, wonderful, excellent, delightful, stupendous
>
> Synonyms for *run:* hurry, rush, race, dash, zip
>
> Synonyms for *say:* reply, explain, exclaim, state, comment

Complete each sentence with a more descriptive word from the word box.

> miniature   stamina   ravenous   rummaged

1. The runner lacked the _____ to complete the marathon.
   (energy)

2. Having not eaten in over a day, the lost hikers were _____.
   (hungry)

3. I viewed the exhibit of _____ carvings with amazement.
   (small)

4. She _____ frantically through the boxes to find her missing ring.
   (looked)

Write two interesting sentences, each using one of the following synonyms for *big*.

> immense   vast   massive   enormous   substantial   gigantic

5. _____

_____

6. _____

_____

> Antonyms are words with opposite meanings.

huge—tiny   gloomy—happy   anxious—calm   enter—exit

Write an antonym for each word.

> receive   weak   tame   high   huge   gloomy   calm   enter

1. anxious _____

2. exit   _____

3. tiny   _____

4. happy   _____

5. strong   _____

6. low   _____

7. give   _____

8. wild   _____

Complete each sentence with an antonym of the word in parentheses ( ).

9. Because I left my books at school, my pack was _____.
(heavy)

10. As I walked home, I felt very _____.
(sad)

11. My mom planned a _____ party for my birthday.
(tiny)

12. I _____ everyone a small present for coming.
(received)

Language Fundamentals • EMC 2754 • © Evan-Moor Corp.

> Use antonyms to compare things.
>
> The view of the mountain is **gorgeous,** but the view of the garbage is **ugly.**
>
> Nick is **delighted,** but Tina is **disappointed.**

Write an antonym for each word.

> jog   ugly   despise   delighted   powerful

1. weak _____

4. disappointed _____

2. gorgeous _____

5. adore _____

3. walk _____

Complete each sentence. Write an antonym for the underlined word.

6. The library is <u>quiet</u>, but the gym is _____.

7. The <u>ancient</u> world is fascinating, but I prefer living in _____ times.

8. Throw the <u>stale</u> roll away and take a _____ one.

9. Most of the laundry is still <u>wet</u>, but this shirt is _____.

10. My mom has to <u>work</u> on weekdays, but she will _____ on the weekend.

> Homophones are words that sound alike but have different spellings and different meanings.
>
> Did you **write** the **right** answer? I wrote "true" **for** number **four**.

Write a homophone for each word.

1. ant _____

2. sent _____

3. new _____

4. write _____

5. sew _____

6. threw _____

7. ate _____

8. no _____

9. pair _____

10. here _____

Write the word that completes the sentence correctly.

11. You need to decide _____ you will go home or not.
                   (weather, whether)

12. "We are _____ to go to the store," I answered.
            (already, all ready)

Write two sentences using the homophones.

13. (piece) _____

_____

14. (peace) _____

_____

> Homophones are words that sound alike but have different spellings and different meanings.

My **aunt,** my mother's sister, hates **ants.**

I **sent** my mom roses because she likes their sweet **scent.**

Circle the homophone that completes the sentence correctly.

1. The waves of the (sea, see) crashed against the shore.

2. Birds flew across the clear (blew, blue) sky.

3. We played for over an (hour, our) before lunch.

4. Then we (eight, ate) our sandwiches.

Write a sentence for each word in parentheses ( ).

5. (brake) _____

_____

6. (break) _____

_____

7. (plain) _____

_____

8. (plane) _____

_____

Fill in the bubble next to the correct answer.

1. Choose the synonym for the underlined word.
   The silly puppy rolled in the mud.

   Ⓐ happy

   Ⓑ dirty

   Ⓒ similar

   Ⓓ foolish

2. Choose the synonym for the underlined word.
   Traffic rushed past the park.

   Ⓐ stated

   Ⓑ walked

   Ⓒ hurried

   Ⓓ crawled

3. Choose the antonym for the underlined word.
   The wild animals were amazing to watch.

   Ⓐ tame

   Ⓑ strong

   Ⓒ gloomy

   Ⓓ anxious

4. Choose the antonym for the underlined word.
   Tony sang a sad song in the concert.

   Ⓐ rough

   Ⓑ wealthy

   Ⓒ gloomy

   Ⓓ cheerful

5. Which pair of words completes the sentence correctly?
   Yes, that is _____ house over _____.

   Ⓐ they're, there

   Ⓑ their, there

   Ⓒ their, they're

   Ⓓ their, their

> A compound word is made up of two smaller words.
>
> **light + house = lighthouse**
>
> A **lighthouse** shined its light from the shore.
>
> **motor + boat = motorboat**
>
> My uncle's **motorboat** makes a lot of noise.

Circle the two words that make up each compound word.

1. toothbrush

2. pineapple

3. headlight

4. playground

5. bookshelf

6. rainbow

7. seashell

8. basketball

Complete each sentence with a compound word formed with two words from the word box.

> corn   boat   pop   pack   coat   back   rain   house

9. Max lived on a _____ on the river.

10. He always wore a bright red _____.

11. He carried a huge _____ full of clothes.

12. He ate _____ while he watched TV.

> Words with the same base word are related in meaning.
>
> The busy intersection had a **sign**al light to stop traffic.
>
> There were **sign**s that named the streets, too.
>
> A traffic officer was **sign**ing a ticket for one motorist.

The words in the word box have the same base word. Circle the base words. Then complete each sentence using a word from the word box.

> placement   misplaced   places   replace   placemats

1. Carly _____ the candles in the center of the table.

2. Then, she puts _____ around the edges.

3. She will _____ the faded flowers in each vase.

4. Finally, she will check the _____ of the silverware.

5. Then, she discovered that she had _____ the name cards.

Write a sentence for each word.

> thank   thankful   unthankful

6. _____

_____

7. _____

_____

8. _____

_____

Language Fundamentals • EMC 2754 • © Evan-Moor Corp.

> Add word endings, such as –s, –ed, –ing, –er, and –est, to base words to make new words.
>
> Lori **talks** with a loud voice.
> Today she **talked** loudly all through lunch.
> Sometimes I think she will never stop **talking.**

Add a word ending to each underlined word to make a word that fits in the sentence.

1. I love the <u>feel</u> _____ of the wind at night.

2. The breeze <u>blow</u> _____ gently across the hills.

3. The <u>tree</u> _____ sway and whisper all night.

4. The North Star <u>sparkle</u> _____ brightly.

5. The <u>bright</u> _____ star seemed to flicker and glow.

6. Today the <u>cloud</u> _____ filled most of the sky.

7. They <u>cover</u> _____ the sun this morning.

8. The sky grew <u>dark</u> _____ as the clouds got thicker.

9. Soon it was <u>rain</u> _____ hard.

10. Tomorrow the <u>strong</u> _____ storm of the year will hit our town.

11. We will be <u>watch</u> _____ from inside.

12. The <u>strong</u> _____ winds can't reach us here.

Add word endings, such as *–s*, *–ed*, *–ing*, *–er*, and *–est* to base words to make new words.

Ellie laugh**s** as we watch the movie.
I laugh**ed** when my cat pounced on a bug.
We were laugh**ing** when the clowns piled out of the car.

The car was small**er** than a normal car.
In fact, it was the small**est** car I'd ever seen!

To complete each sentence, add an ending to each word in parentheses ( ).

1. _____ is my favorite thing to do.
   (draw)

2. Whenever there's been a contest, I've _____ one of my pictures.
   (enter)

3. I even _____ a picture of our house.
   (paint)

4. When I get _____, I want to be an architect.
   (old)

5. I like to study the _____ buildings in the world.
   (tall)

6. The Empire State Building is _____ than the Eiffel Tower.
   (tall)

7. Last year, I _____ buildings in Hong Kong.
   (research)

8. My friend _____ buildings every year.
   (research)

> Sometimes, a word's meaning can be determined from other words around it. In this example, *spectacular* means "magnificent." The second sentence gives a clue to its meaning.
>
> The fireworks were **spectacular.** I had never seen such a **magnificent** sight!

Circle the word or words that help you figure out the meaning of the underlined word.

1. We were <u>anticipating</u> a great game last Friday. I look forward to going.

2. The team was really <u>psyched</u>. Everyone was eager to show we could win.

3. My brother was really worried. He <u>agonized</u> over his solo.

4. My brother is some kind of <u>virtuoso</u>. Everyone says he's a musical genius.

5. I'm <u>content</u> to play ball. Whether I'm batting or in the field, I'm happy.

6. Still, I spend a lot of time on my homework. I'm as <u>studious</u> as the next guy.

7. My mom says my brother and I are <u>fortunate</u>. Life is good for us.

8. We have lots of <u>options</u> for the future. Not everyone has as many choices as we do.

Write the meaning of the bolded word.

9. We need to **reconvene** tomorrow. Let's get together again at 9:00 a.m.

   The word *reconvene* means "_____."

10. Maybe next time we'll **triumph** over the other team. I know we can win.

    The word *triumph* means "_____."

> Sometimes, a word's meaning can be determined from the other words and groups of words around it.
>
> Laura **persisted** until she had mastered the video game.
>
> *Persisted* means "did not give up."

Read each sentence. Then write what the underlined word means.

1. It used to be hard to hike in that park, but now it's <u>effortless</u>.

   The word *effortless* means "_____."

2. The trails that were <u>deserted</u> yesterday are now filled with hikers.

   The word *deserted* means "_____."

3. The <u>obstacles</u> are gone. The paths are clear.

   The word *obstacles* means "_____."

4. We <u>contributed</u> to the Clean Up Our Park drive. We washed cars to earn money.

   The word *contributed* means "_____."

5. Now that the litter has been removed, the area looks <u>pristine</u>.

   The word *pristine* means "_____."

6. We used to go to the park only occasionally. Now we go <u>frequently</u>.

   The word *frequently* means "_____."

Language Fundamentals • EMC 2754 • © Evan-Moor Corp.

Fill in the bubble next to the correct answer.

1. Which of these words is a compound word?

Ⓐ fullness

Ⓑ brightest

Ⓒ fabulous

Ⓓ bookshelf

2. Mark the word that has the same base word as these words.
thanks   thanked   thanking   thankless

Ⓐ tank

Ⓑ through

Ⓒ thinking

Ⓓ thankful

3. Which word completes the sentence correctly?
Darren _____ whenever he is asked.

Ⓐ helps

Ⓑ helpful

Ⓒ helping

Ⓓ helper

4. Which word does <u>not</u> have the same base word as the others?

Ⓐ laughs

Ⓑ lampshade

Ⓒ laughing

Ⓓ laughed

5. Which word has a similar meaning to the underlined word?
The <u>clamor</u> of the crowd was deafening.

Ⓐ noise

Ⓑ quiet

Ⓒ silliness

Ⓓ coughing

Proofreading Marks

Use these marks to show corrections.

Mark	Meaning	Example
ℒ	Take this out (delete).	I love ~~to~~ to read.
⊙	Add a period.	It was late⊙
≡	Make this a capital letter.	First prize went to m̲aria.
/	Make this a lowercase letter.	We saw a B̸lack C̸at.
——	Fix the spelling.	This is our ~~hause~~ house.
⋏	Add a comma.	Goodnight⋏ Mom.
⌄	Add an apostrophe.	That⌄s Lil⌄s bike.
⌄ ⌄	Add quotation marks.	⌄Come in,⌄ he said.
! ? ⋀ ⋀	Add an exclamation point or a question mark.	Help⋀! Can you help me⋀?
⋀̄	Add a hyphen.	I've read three⋀̄fourths of the book.
⌒	Close the space.	Foot⌒ball is fun.
⋀	Add a word or letter.	The ⋀red pen is mine.
——	Underline the words.	We read <u>Old Yeller</u>.
⋀̣	Add a colon.	Alex arrived at 4⋀̣00.

Language Fundamentals • EMC 2754 • © Evan-Moor Corp.

Proofread this paragraph. Use proofreading marks to correct the 10 errors.
Hint: One two-word proper noun is counted as one error.

Have you seen Abigails new kite? It's in the shape of a big orange Fish.

She won it at Henrys party last month. Today she and her parentses took the

kite to riverside park to fly it. Josh Jensen and his family went along, too, and

josh brought a kite of his own. The family's had a picnic, and then they flew

Abigails and Josh' kites. On the way home, they stopped at the jensen's house

for ice cream.

Write the errors correctly on the lines.

1. _____

2. _____

3. _____

4. _____

5. _____

6. _____

7. _____

8. _____

9. _____

10. _____

Proofread this paragraph. Find the 10 errors, cross them out, and write the words correctly above them.

My mother's family comes from China, so last summer, my parents, my littleest sister, and I went to China. We wanted to visit our chinese relatives. We landed in Hong Kong, where more of them live. Hong Kong is a biggest city with many more people than San Francisco, where my family lives. Hong Kong is the most big city I've ever visited. We were able to buy many things for very little money, since american prices are much high than Hong Kong prices. Auntie Mu Tan and Uncle Gim live on the Kowloon Peninsula in an area called Yau Ma Tei. Auntie Mu Tan says that's where the better shops are. I found a japanese doll there that I wanted to buy, but my aunt said I should buy something that I could find only in Hong Kong. I ended up buying the prettyest Chinese silk dress I'd ever seen, and it was made by one of the women in the shops near my aunt and uncle's house.

Name _____

Proofread these paragraphs. Find the 10 errors, cross them out, and write the words correctly above them. Hint: A two-word proper adjective is counted as one error.

There are more bodies of water in the United States. There are big bays and biger lakes. The oceans on both sides of the country are the two bigger oceans on Earth. The Pacific Ocean is the larger ocean in the world. The Atlantic Ocean is small than the Pacific, but it is the second-larger ocean on Earth.

The Missouri is the most long river in the United States. However, the egypt river the Nile, the south american river the Amazon, and the chinaese river the Yangtze are longer.

Proofread this paragraph. Use proofreading marks to correct the 10 errors.

Philippe is a new student in ours class. He comes from Lyon, a town in France. His family is French, but them speak English very well. Philippe's father is a chef in a French restaurant here. Me and my family have eaten there twice because they started working there. Mom orders for Dad, mine sister, and I because she can say the names of the dishes. Me and my sister ordered the same thing both times. I can't say the French name yet, but it's called Lamb in Parsley in English. My's mom told my sister her didn't have to eat it all if she didn't like it. My sister ate every last bite of her's. So did I!

Write the errors correctly on the lines.

1. _____

2. _____

3. _____

4. _____

5. _____

6. _____

7. _____

8. _____

9. _____

10. _____

Language Fundamentals • EMC 2754 • © Evan-Moor Corp.

Proofread these paragraphs. Find the 10 errors, cross them out, and write the words correctly above them.

Caleb and Jenny are best friends. Him and her do everything together. When Caleb signed up for swimming lessons, Jenny sent in hers application. When Jenny started helping Mrs. Toyama clean up his yard, Caleb jumped right in to help. Every Saturday, their help Mrs. Toyama for a couple of hours. Her has a huge yard, and now that her kids are grown, she needs help keeping them up.

Jenny mows the lawn usually. Caleb pulls weeds and trims the bushes. She takes breaks when he gets tired and talks to Mrs. Toyama about her life back in Japan. Her and her husband moved to Chicago 45 years ago to go to college. Dr. Toyama is retired now and has health problems. Sometimes when he feels up to it, they joins Caleb, Jenny, and Mrs. Toyama on the porch for tea and cookies. They're time together is always interesting.

Name _____

Proofread these paragraphs. Find the 10 errors, cross them out, and write the words correctly above them.

Kaya had always want a horse, but she and her family live in a house with a small backyard. No matter how much Kaya beged her mother for a horse, the answer were always the same: No room! One day at school, Kaya was talk to her teacher about how much she love horses.

"I love horses, too," Ms. Nakai said. "That's why I volunteer at Kids for Horses. It was a group that helps kids and horses help each other. Does you want to find out more about it?"

"That would be great," Kaya replyed. And that's how Kaya becomed an active volunteer at Kids for Horses, helping many horses find families to take good care of them.

Proofread this paragraph. Use proofreading marks to correct the 10 errors.

Have you ever studyed the living things you can find at the seashore? There is sea urchins, crabs, sea horses, and sand dollars. I has always loved watching the crabs. They are so funny, with the way they walks and their funny legs. My whole family watch them when we go to the beach. We has a contest to see who can find the most crabs. My sister Carrie founded the most the last time we went. The next visit, I will have been the one to find the most. Carrie breaked my dad's record of 15, but I'm going to breaks hers.

Write the errors correctly on the lines.

1. _____

2. _____

3. _____

4. _____

5. _____

6. _____

7. _____

8. _____

9. _____

10. _____

Proofread these paragraphs. Find the 10 errors, cross them out, and write the words correctly above them.

Olivia were so frustrated! She had studied all week for the test in Language Arts. She readed the book twice and then go over it again and again, thinking about what might be on the test. She memorizes the names of the people in the story. She write questions about the book and answered them. She haved her brother Jamie quiz her on the main themes in the story.

When Olivia gotten to school on Friday, she feeled good. When she started the test, she can't believe her eyes. She had studied the wrong book! Mr. Kerman was so nice about it. He telled Olivia she could retake the test the next week.

Language Fundamentals • EMC 2754 • © Evan-Moor Corp.

Proofread these paragraphs. Use proofreading marks to correct the 10 errors.

Graciela was the best soccer player in fifth grade at her school. She want to be the best fifth-grade player in the county, so she practiced every day after school. Sometimes she practice with her team, and sometimes she do it on her own.

The next game was go well, until Graciela slipped in the mud on the field and falled. "Ow!" she cryed as she hitted the ground. Everyone rushed over to check on Graciela. "I'm OK," she said as she slowly gots up. After she rested on the bench for a while, Graciela is ready to go back into the game. That day, she kick the winning goal. She was finally the best player in the county.

Write the errors correctly on the lines.

1. _____

2. _____

3. _____

4. _____

5. _____

6. _____

7. _____

8. _____

9. _____

10. _____

Proofread this paragraph. Use proofreading marks to correct the 10 errors.

   I can't listen to Irish fiddle music without happy tapping my feet. My Aunt Maura has played the fiddle for a verry long time, and she plays very good. She performs regular at Celtic music festivals. People crowd eager near the stage to watch the fiddlers in action. There are usual dancers on stage, too. The faster the fiddlers play, the quicklier the dancers dance. I'm studying Irish step dancing. I want to dance more better than my sister, Colleen, but that's going to take practice. I've not never seen a better dancer than Colleen, but someday people will be singing my praises loud, too!

Write the errors correctly on the lines.

1. _____

2. _____

3. _____

4. _____

5. _____

6. _____

7. _____

8. _____

9. _____

10. _____

Language Fundamentals • EMC 2754 • © Evan-Moor Corp.

Proofread this paragraph. Correct the incomplete sentences by adding words to make them complete. Write the corrected paragraph on the lines below.

What's your favorite National Park? Mine Yosemite. Our first time there camped in the valley. We El Capitan from almost everywhere. Is like a big stone mountain. Looks as if half of it has been cut away. The next time we stayed in Tuolumne Meadows, which is a big open field. Yosemite is beautiful, whichever way you see it.

_____

_____

_____

_____

_____

_____

_____

_____

_____

_____

Name _____

Find each run-on sentence and correct it. You can create two sentences or make the run-on sentence into a compound or complex sentence, using conjunctions. Write the corrected paragraph on the lines below.

Have you ever seen a tornado heading your way it's a very scary sight! The tornado looks like a big, dark funnel tornadoes can happen anywhere in the U.S. about 1,000 tornadoes are reported from all over the country every year. A tornado can travel at speeds up to 250 miles per hour or more it can cause damage in a path that is up to a mile wide and 50 miles long. You should research what to do in case of a tornado you will know what to do. Be prepared stay safe.

_____

_____

_____

_____

_____

_____

_____

_____

Language Fundamentals • EMC 2754 • © Evan-Moor Corp.

Read the paragraph and then rewrite it on the lines below to make it read more smoothly. Combine sentences to avoid choppiness and unnecessary repetition.

Lucy was an only child. Lucy had been an only child for six years. One day, her parents told her something. They told her that she was going to have a baby brother. Everyone in the family was really excited. They were excited about the baby. Lucy wasn't sure. She wasn't sure about having a little brother. Then one day her parents went to the hospital. They went there to have the baby. Lucy went to the hospital the next day. She got to hold the baby. The baby was fussing. Lucy started to hum to him. He stopped crying. Having a little brother might be pretty cool after all!

_____

_____

_____

_____

_____

_____

_____

_____

Proofread this paragraph. Use proofreading marks to correct the 10 errors.

My brother juan and I love to watch old movies, and I mean really old movies! My brother is 12 and I'm 10, but we watch movies that were made before my parents were born! Juan likes the dance movies with fred Astaire, who was a famous movie star in the 1930s and 1940s. I like musicals, too, and my favorite is called <u>West Side story</u>. My birthday is in march, and Juan bought me a DVD. it's called <u>Funny face</u>, and it stars Fred Astaire and audrey Hepburn. Audrey Hepburn is one of my favorite actresses. My birthday was on a saturday, so Juan and I stayed up late and watched the movie. Juan's birthday is august 23. There is a festival of old movies in New york City on that day, so we're going to go for his birthday.

Write the errors correctly on the lines.

1. _____   6. _____

2. _____   7. _____

3. _____   8. _____

4. _____   9. _____

5. _____   10. _____

Language Fundamentals • EMC 2754 • © Evan-Moor Corp.

Name _____

Proofread these paragraphs. Correct any errors and add any missing punctuation.

Minas Aunt Farida is teaching Mina and her brother, Badri, to cook Aunt Farida is known throughout the neighborhood for her fantastic cooking

Mina loves fish chicken and lamb, so her aunt is teaching her how to make some special dishes for each type of meat. Badris favorite dishes are made with vegetables because he doesnt eat meat. Aunt Farida taught him to make a dish that calls for 450 gm of green beans! That sounds like a lot, but its really only 1 lbs. Mina likes chili peppers but Badri doesn't like his food too hot.

Do you know what the best part of a cooking lesson is You get to eat everything you cook!

Write the corrected second paragraph on the lines below.
Remember to include the correct punctuation.

_____

_____

_____

_____

_____

_____

_____

Proofread these paragraphs. Correct any errors and add any missing punctuation.

Darrell and his mother were meeting Darrells father at Grand Central Station. They had just moved to New York and they weren't familiar with the station Mrs Williams went up to the information window. "Excuse me, she asked the woman in the booth. "Can you tell me when the train from White Plains arrives"

"The next one is due in at 417 on Track 19" she replied.

Where is that?" asked Mrs. Williams.

Right over there," the woman replied, pointing to the stairs leading to the track.

They looked at where the woman was pointing and there was Darrell's father coming up the stairs. It was a happy reunion for all!

Write the corrected first paragraph on the lines below.
Remember to include the correct punctuation.

_____

_____

_____

_____

_____

_____

Name _____

Proofread this paragraph. Correct any errors and add any missing punctuation.

After school lets out at 245, Elena and Rodrigo help Mr Wey shelve books in the school library They help sort the books and then they put the books on shelves where they belong. They also put magazines newspapers and paperbacks where they belong. Why do they work in the library They both like to read and this way they get to see the latest books when they come in. Elena's favorite book is A Wrinkle in Time by Madeleine L'Engle. Rodrigo's favorite book is Breaking Through by Francisco Jiménez.

Write the paragraph correctly on the lines below.
Remember to include all of your corrections.

_____

_____

_____

_____

_____

_____

_____

_____

_____

Proofread this business letter. Correct any errors and add any missing punctuation marks.

Lourdes Posadas

47 79th Street

Allentown, pa

May 7 2007

Wendell Sporting Goods

171 Randall Ave

Kansas City MO

To Whom It May Concern

I purchased a Frost Proof parka at your store on April 16 2007 and I would like

to bring something to your attention The tag on the parka said that the jacket was

waterproof. I wore the jacket in a rainstorm the week after I bought it and I got soaked!

I am returning the jacket, and I would appreciate a refund of the $97.99 that I paid

for it. Please send it to the address above. Thank you for your help with this.

Sincerely

Lourdes Posadas

Language Fundamentals • EMC 2754 • © Evan-Moor Corp.

Read these paragraphs. Cross out any errors and correct them above the crossed out words.

Geri is a wonderful artist. She has been drawing since she could hold a crayon. Geri doesn't know nothing about sports, but she can tell you everything about a ancient painter called Giotto. Giotto painted something called "frescos," or paintings on walls. Its amazing how they've lasted over the centuries. Geri paints very good herself. Their are many galleries that show her paintings.

Geri says, "You have to follow you're heart and do what you love. Were always rushing around, trying to succeed. The way to succeed is to do what makes you happy."

Geri knows that if you do what matters too you, you'll do it good "Its what is in your heart that's important," she says.

Proofread these paragraphs. Find the 10 errors, cross them out, and write the words correctly above them.

Carter plays baseball really good. They're is nothing he likes better than batting the ball around. He and his sister, Alexis, love to play in there backyard. Carter hits, while Alexis catches. There isn't nobody in the Roseville Kids' League who catches better than Alexis. She can catch an fly ball from anywhere in the field.

On Wednesday, the Kids' League sent out it's list for the All-Star Game. "Your not going to believe what happened," Carter told Alex. "Both of us have been chosen to play in the All-Star Game. This is well for both of us," he continued.

"Were going to get a chance to show everyone how good we are," Alexis said. "That's what teamwork will do for you. Its great to get to do this together!"

Language Fundamentals • EMC 2754 • © Evan-Moor Corp.

Answer Key

Page 11

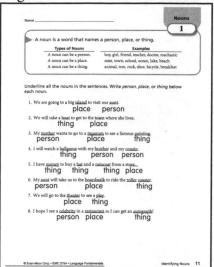

Nouns 1

> A noun is a word that names a person, place, or thing.

Types of Nouns	Examples
A noun can be a person.	boy, girl, friend, teacher, doctor, mechanic
A noun can be a place.	state, town, school, ocean, lake, beach
A noun can be a thing.	animal, tree, rock, shoe, bicycle, breakfast

Underline all the nouns in the sentences. Write *person, place,* or *thing* below each noun.

1. We are going to a big island to visit our aunt.
       place   person
2. We will take a boat to get to the town where she lives.
       thing   place
3. My mother wants to go to a museum to see a famous painting.
   person   place   thing
4. I will watch a ballgame with my brother and my cousin.
       thing   person   person
5. I have money to buy a hat and a raincoat from a store.
       thing   thing   thing   place
6. My aunt will take us to the boardwalk to ride the roller coaster.
     person   place   thing
7. We will go to the theater to see a play.
       place   thing
8. I hope I see a celebrity in a restaurant so I can get an autograph!
     person   place   thing

Identifying Nouns 11

Page 12

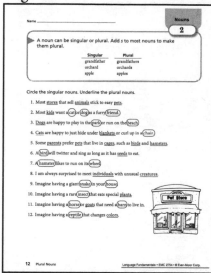

Nouns 2

> A noun can be singular or plural. Add *s* to most nouns to make them plural.

Singular	Plural
grandfather	grandfathers
orchard	orchards
apple	apples

Circle the singular nouns. Underline the plural nouns.

1. Most stores that sell animals stick to easy pets.
2. Most kids want a cat or dog as a furry friend.
3. Dogs are happy to play in the park or run on the beach.
4. Cats are happy to just hide under blankets or curl up in a chair.
5. Some parents prefer pets that live in cages, such as birds and hamsters.
6. A bird will twitter and sing as long as it has seeds to eat.
7. A hamster likes to run on its wheel.
8. I am always surprised to meet individuals with unusual creatures.
9. Imagine having a giant snake in your house.
10. Imagine having a rare insect that eats special plants.
11. Imagine having a horse or goats that need a barn to live in.
12. Imagine having a reptile that changes colors.

12 Plural Nouns

Page 13

Nouns 3

> Add *es* to singular nouns that end in *sh, ch, x, s,* and *z* to form the plural.

Singular	Plural
bush	bushes
church	churches
tax	taxes
class	classes
waltz	waltzes

Complete each sentence with the plural form of a word from the word box.

> klutz box wish dress sandwich
> boss patch fox glass toothbrush

1. We have many **boxes** of things to pack.
2. We have plates, **glasses** and silverware to pack.
3. We sometimes act like **klutzes** but let's not break anything today!
4. We can pack our own clothing, such as shirts, pants, and **dresses**
5. Let's throw away clothes that are ripped or have **patches**
6. Don't pack things we will need tonight, such as our **toothbrushes**
7. Please make some **sandwiches** to eat on the long drive.
8. Don't forget the travel games and the baby's favorite book about **foxes**
9. We are packing because our mom's **bosses** offered her a new job.
10. She followed their **wishes** and now we are moving to another state.

Singular and Plural Nouns 13

Page 14

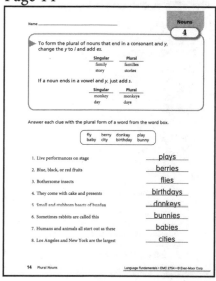

Nouns 4

> To form the plural of nouns that end in a consonant and *y*, change the *y* to *i* and add *es*.

Singular	Plural
family	families
story	stories

> If a noun ends in a vowel and *y*, just add *s*.

Singular	Plural
monkey	monkeys
day	days

Answer each clue with the plural form of a word from the word box.

> fly berry donkey play
> baby city birthday bunny

1. Live performances on stage   **plays**
2. Blue, black, or red fruits   **berries**
3. Bothersome insects   **flies**
4. They come with cake and presents   **birthdays**
5. Small and stubborn beasts of burden   **donkeys**
6. Sometimes rabbits are called this   **bunnies**
7. Humans and animals all start out as these   **babies**
8. Los Angeles and New York are the largest   **cities**

14 Plural Nouns

Page 15

Nouns 5

> Some nouns have irregular plural forms. Practice these nouns and learn their spellings.

Singular Noun	Irregular Plural
mouse	mice
goose	geese
ox	oxen
tooth	teeth
child	children
woman	women
man	men

Read each sentence. Circle *Correct* if the sentence is correct. Circle *Incorrect* if it is incorrect. Rewrite each incorrect sentence correctly on the line below it.

1. There are many child watching the parade today.   Correct   **Incorrect**
   There are many children watching the parade today.
2. Everyone loves to float with the huge mouse on it.   **Correct**   Incorrect
3. There are live goose in cages on the wagon.   Correct   **Incorrect**
   There are live geese in cages on the wagon.
4. Suddenly, a group of woman screamed.   Correct   **Incorrect**
   Suddenly, a group of women screamed.
5. Two real mouse skittered across the street.   Correct   **Incorrect**
   Two real mice skittered across the street.

Irregular Plural Nouns 15

Page 16

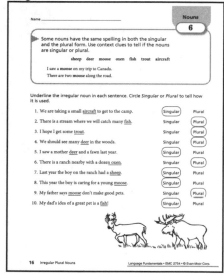

Nouns 6

> Some nouns have the same spelling in both the singular and the plural form. Use context clues to tell if the nouns are singular or plural.

> sheep deer moose oxen fish trout aircraft

> I saw a **moose** on my trip to Canada.
> There are two **moose** along the road.

Underline the irregular noun in each sentence. Circle *Singular* or *Plural* to tell how it is used.

1. We are taking a small aircraft to get to the camp.   **Singular**   Plural
2. There is a stream where we will catch many fish.   Singular   **Plural**
3. I hope I get some trout.   **Singular**   Plural
4. We should see many deer in the woods.   Singular   **Plural**
5. I saw a mother deer and a fawn last year.   **Singular**   Plural
6. There is a ranch nearby with a dozen oxen.   Singular   **Plural**
7. Last year the boy on the ranch had a sheep.   **Singular**   Plural
8. This year the boy is caring for a young moose.   **Singular**   Plural
9. My father says moose don't make good pets.   Singular   **Plural**
10. My dad's idea of a great pet is a fish!   **Singular**   Plural

16 Irregular Plural Nouns

Page 17

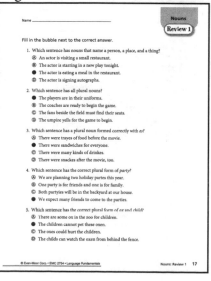

Nouns Review 1

Fill in the bubble next to the correct answer.

1. Which sentence has nouns that name a person, a place, and a thing?
   - Ⓐ An actor is visiting a small restaurant.
   - Ⓑ The actor is starring in a new play tonight.
   - ● The actor is eating a meal in the restaurant.
   - Ⓓ The actor is signing autographs.
2. Which sentence has all plural nouns?
   - ● The players are in their uniforms.
   - Ⓑ The coaches are ready to begin the game.
   - Ⓒ The fans beside the field must find their seats.
   - Ⓓ The umpire yells for the game to begin.
3. Which sentence has a plural noun formed correctly with *es*?
   - Ⓐ There were trays of food before the movie.
   - ● There were sandwiches for everyone.
   - Ⓒ There were many kinds of drinkes.
   - Ⓓ There were snackes after the movie, too.
4. Which sentence has the correct plural form of *party*?
   - Ⓐ We are planning two holiday partes this year.
   - Ⓑ One party is for friends and one is for family.
   - Ⓒ Both partyies will be in the backyard at our house.
   - ● We expect many friends to come to the parties.
5. Which sentence has the correct plural form of *ox* and *child*?
   - Ⓐ There are some ox in the zoo for children.
   - ● The children cannot pet these oxen.
   - Ⓒ The oxes could hurt the children.
   - Ⓓ The childs can watch the oxen from behind the fence.

Nouns: Review 1 17

Page 18

Nouns 7

> A possessive noun shows belonging. For singular nouns, add an apostrophe and *s* (*'s*) to make the noun possessive.

Singular Noun	Singular Possessive	Example
mother	mother's	mother's baby
cat	cat's	cat's tail
book	book's	book's title
country	country's	country's leader

Read the sentences. Underline the possessive nouns. Circle any nouns that should be possessive. Write those nouns correctly on the lines.

1. Our teacher's friend is a famous author.
2. The author's new book is on display in the library.
3. The librarian said the writer visit is next week.   **writer's**
4. Our class turn reviewing the book is tomorrow.   **class's**
5. Kids who have read it say the story's plot is exciting.
6. I hear the book ending is very surprising.   **book's**
7. My friend favorite character is the detective.   **friend's**
8. The detective role is important in the book.   **detective's**
9. I would like to study the artist's pictures.
10. I hear one picture clues can solve the mystery!   **picture's**

18 Singular Possessive Nouns

Page 19

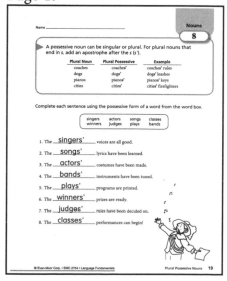

Nouns 8

> A possessive noun can be singular or plural. For plural nouns that end in *s*, add an apostrophe after the *s* (*s'*).

Plural Noun	Plural Possessive	Example
coaches	coaches'	coaches' rules
dogs	dogs'	dogs' leashes
pianos	pianos'	pianos' keys
cities	cities'	cities' firefighters

Complete each sentence using the possessive form of a word from the word box.

> singers actors songs classes
> winners judges plays bands

1. The **singers'** voices are all good.
2. The **songs'** lyrics have been learned.
3. The **actors'** costumes have been made.
4. The **bands'** instruments have been tuned.
5. The **plays'** programs are printed.
6. The **winners'** prizes are ready.
7. The **judges'** rules have been decided on.
8. The **classes'** performances can begin!

Plural Possessive Nouns 19

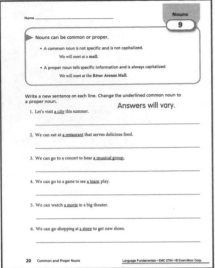

Nouns 9

Nouns can be common or proper.
- A common noun is not specific and is not capitalized.
  We will meet at a mall.
- A proper noun tells specific information and is always capitalized.
  We will meet at the River Avenue Mall.

Write a new sentence on each line. Change the underlined common noun to a proper noun.   Answers will vary.

1. Let's visit a city this summer.
2. We can eat at a restaurant that serves delicious food.
3. We can go to a concert to hear a musical group.
4. We can go to a game to see a team play.
5. We can watch a movie in a big theater.
6. We can go shopping at a store to get new shoes.

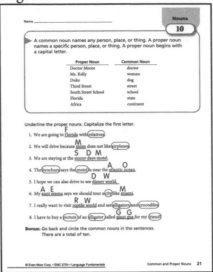

Nouns 10

A common noun names any person, place, or thing. A proper noun names a specific person, place, or thing. A proper noun begins with a capital letter.

Proper Noun	Common Noun
Doctor Moore	doctor
Ms. Kelly	woman
Duke	dog
Third Street	street
South Street School	school
Florida	state
Africa	continent

Underline the proper nouns. Capitalize the first letter.

1. We are going to florida with relatives.
2. We will drive because mom does not like airplanes.
3. We are staying at the sunny days motel.
4. The brochure says the motel is near the atlantic ocean.
5. I hope we can also drive to see disney world.
6. My aunt emma says we should tour a city like miami.
7. I really want to visit reptile world and see alligators and crocodiles.
8. I have to buy a picture of an alligator called giant gus for my friend!

Bonus: Go back and circle the common nouns in the sentences. There are a total of ten.

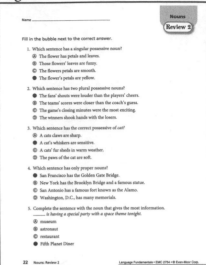

Nouns Review 2

Fill in the bubble next to the correct answer.

1. Which sentence has a singular possessive noun?
   - Ⓐ The flower has petals and leaves.
   - Ⓑ Those flowers' leaves are fuzzy.
   - Ⓒ The flowers petals are smooth.
   - ● The flower's petals are yellow.

2. Which sentence has two plural possessive nouns?
   - ● The fans' shouts were louder than the players' cheers.
   - Ⓑ The teams' scores were closer than the coach's guess.
   - Ⓒ The game's closing minutes were the most exciting.
   - Ⓓ The winners shook hands with the losers.

3. Which sentence has the correct possessive of *cat*?
   - Ⓐ A cats claws are sharp.
   - ● A cat's whiskers are sensitive.
   - Ⓒ A cats' fur sheds in warm weather.
   - Ⓓ The paws of the cat are soft.

4. Which sentence has only proper nouns?
   - ● San Francisco has the Golden Gate Bridge.
   - Ⓑ New York has the Brooklyn Bridge and a famous statue.
   - Ⓒ San Antonio has a famous fort known as the Alamo.
   - Ⓓ Washington, D.C., has many memorials.

5. Complete the sentence with the noun that gives the most information.
   _____ is having a special party with a space theme tonight.
   - Ⓐ museum
   - Ⓑ astronaut
   - Ⓒ restaurant
   - ● Fifth Planet Diner

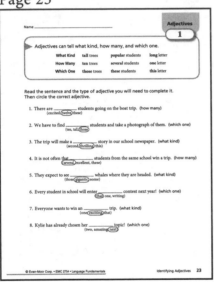

Adjectives 1

Adjectives can tell what kind, how many, and which one.

What Kind	tall trees	popular students	long letter
How Many	ten trees	several students	one letter
Which One	those trees	these students	this letter

Read the sentence and the type of adjective you will need to complete it. Then circle the correct adjective.

1. There are _____ students going on the boat trip. (how many)
   (excited, twelve, these)
2. We have to find _____ students and take a photograph of them. (which one)
   (ten, tall, those)
3. The trip will make a _____ story in our school newspaper. (what kind)
   (second, thrilling, this)
4. It is not often that _____ students from the same school win a trip. (how many)
   (several, excellent, these)
5. They expect to see _____ whales where they are headed. (what kind)
   (those, gigantic, some)
6. Every student in school will enter _____ contest next year! (which one)
   (that, one, writing)
7. Everyone wants to win an _____ trip. (what kind)
   (one, exciting, that)
8. Kylie has already chosen her _____ topic! (which one)
   (two, amazing, next)

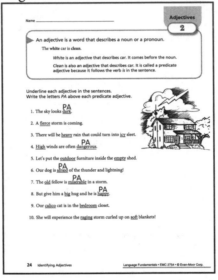

Adjectives 2

An adjective is a word that describes a noun or a pronoun.

The white car is clean.

White is an adjective that describes *car*. It comes before the noun.

Clean is also an adjective that describes *car*. It is called a predicate adjective because it follows the verb *is* in the sentence.

Underline each adjective in the sentences. Write the letters *PA* above each predicate adjective.

1. The sky looks dark. PA
2. A fierce storm is coming.
3. There will be heavy rain that could turn into icy sleet.
4. High winds are often dangerous. PA
5. Let's put the outdoor furniture in the empty shed.
6. Our dog is afraid of the thunder and lightning! PA
7. The old fellow is miserable in a storm. PA
8. But give him a big hug and he is happy. PA
9. Our calico cat is in the bedroom closet.
10. She will experience the raging storm curled up on soft blankets!

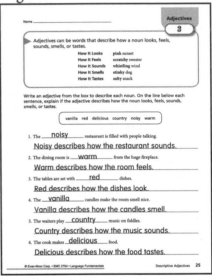

Adjectives 3

Adjectives can be words that describe how a noun looks, feels, sounds, smells, or tastes.

How It Looks	pink sunset
How It Feels	scratchy sweater
How It Sounds	whistling wind
How It Smells	stinky dog
How It Tastes	salty snack

Write an adjective from the box to describe each noun. On the line below each sentence, explain if the adjective describes how the noun looks, feels, sounds, smells, or tastes.

vanilla   red   delicious   country   noisy   warm

1. The **noisy** restaurant is filled with people talking.
   Noisy describes how the restaurant sounds.
2. The dining room is **warm** from the huge fireplace.
   Warm describes how the room feels.
3. The tables are set with **red** dishes.
   Red describes how the dishes look.
4. The **vanilla** candles make the room smell nice.
   Vanilla describes how the candles smell.
5. The waiters play **country** music on fiddles.
   Country describes how the music sounds.
6. The cook makes **delicious** food.
   Delicious describes how the food tastes.

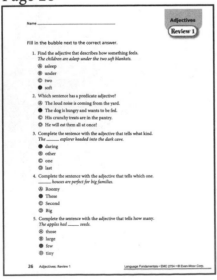

Adjectives Review 1

Fill in the bubble next to the correct answer.

1. Find the adjective that describes how something feels.
   The children are asleep under the two soft blankets.
   - Ⓐ asleep
   - Ⓑ under
   - Ⓒ two
   - ● soft

2. Which sentence has a predicate adjective?
   - Ⓐ The loud noise is coming from the yard.
   - ● The dog is hungry and wants to be fed.
   - Ⓒ His crunchy treats are in the pantry.
   - Ⓓ He will eat them all at once!

3. Complete the sentence with the adjective that tells what kind.
   The _____ explorer headed into the dark cave.
   - ● daring
   - Ⓑ other
   - Ⓒ one
   - Ⓓ last

4. Complete the sentence with the adjective that tells which one.
   _____ houses are perfect for big families.
   - Ⓐ Roomy
   - ● These
   - Ⓒ Second
   - Ⓓ Big

5. Complete the sentence with the adjective that tells how many.
   The apples had _____ seeds.
   - Ⓐ those
   - Ⓑ large
   - ● few
   - Ⓓ tiny

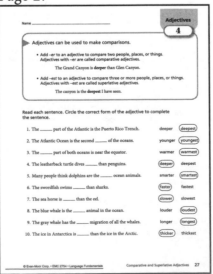

Adjectives 4

Adjectives can be used to make comparisons.
- Add –er to an adjective to compare two people, places, or things. Adjectives with –er are called comparative adjectives.
  The Grand Canyon is deeper than Glen Canyon.
- Add –est to an adjective to compare three or more people, places, or things. Adjectives with –est are called superlative adjectives.
  The canyon is the deepest I have seen.

Read each sentence. Circle the correct form of the adjective to complete the sentence.

1. The _____ part of the Atlantic is the Puerto Rico Trench.   deeper   (deepest)
2. The Atlantic Ocean is the second _____ of the oceans.   younger   (youngest)
3. The _____ part of both oceans is near the equator.   warmer   (warmest)
4. The leatherback turtle dives _____ than penguins.   (deeper)   deepest
5. Many people think dolphins are the _____ ocean animals.   smarter   (smartest)
6. The swordfish swims _____ than sharks.   (faster)   fastest
7. The sea horse is _____ than the eel.   (slower)   slowest
8. The blue whale is the _____ animal in the ocean.   louder   (loudest)
9. The gray whale has the _____ migration of all the whales.   longer   (longest)
10. The ice in Antarctica is _____ than the ice in the Arctic.   (thicker)   thickest

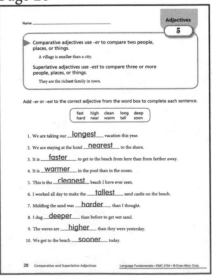

Adjectives 5

Comparative adjectives use –er to compare two people, places, or things.
  A village is smaller than a city.

Superlative adjectives use –est to compare three or more people, places, or things.
  They are the richest family in town.

Add –er or –est to the correct adjective from the word box to complete each sentence.

fast   high   clean   deep
hard   near   warm   tall   long   soon

1. We are taking our **longest** vacation this year.
2. We are staying at the hotel **nearest** to the shore.
3. It is **faster** to get to the beach from here than from farther away.
4. It is **warmer** in the pool than in the ocean.
5. This is the **cleanest** beach I have ever seen.
6. I worked all day to make the **tallest** sand castle on the beach.
7. Molding the sand was **harder** than I thought.
8. I dug **deeper** than before to get wet sand.
9. The waves are **higher** than they were yesterday.
10. We got to the beach **sooner** today.

Page 29

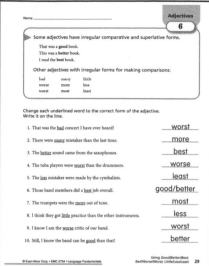

Name _____

Adjectives
6

Some adjectives have irregular comparative and superlative forms.

That was a **good** book.
This was a **better** book.
I read the **best** book.

Other adjectives with irregular forms for making comparisons.

bad	many	little
worse	more	less
worst	most	least

Change each underlined word to the correct form of the adjective.
Write it on the line.

1. That was the <u>bad</u> concert I have ever heard! — **worst**
2. There were <u>many</u> mistakes than the last time. — **more**
3. The <u>better</u> sound came from the saxophones. — **best**
4. The tuba players were <u>worst</u> than the drummers. — **worse**
5. The <u>less</u> mistakes were made by the cymbalists. — **least**
6. Those band members did a <u>best</u> job overall. — **good/better**
7. The trumpets were the <u>more</u> out of tune. — **most**
8. I think they got <u>little</u> practice than the other instruments. — **less**
9. I know I am the <u>worse</u> critic of our band. — **worst**
10. Still, I know the band can be <u>good</u> than that! — **better**

© Evan-Moor Corp. • EMC 2754 • Language Fundamentals
Using Good/Better/Best;
Bad/Worse/Worst; Little/Less/Least 29

Page 30

Name _____

Adjectives
Review 2

Fill in the bubble next to the correct answer.

1. Complete the sentence with the correct form of the adjective.
   Those clouds are the _____ in the sky.
   Ⓐ dark
   Ⓑ darker
   ● darkest
   Ⓓ darkening

2. Which sentence is correct?
   ● I ordered the worst sandwich on the menu.
   Ⓑ She has the better pie of all.
   Ⓒ His food was best than mine.
   Ⓓ Our food was worser than his.

3. Which adjective would be used to compare two stars?
   Ⓐ bright
   ● brighter
   Ⓒ brightest
   Ⓓ brighten

4. Which sentence is correct?
   ● Whales are the largest mammals.
   Ⓑ Whales are the larger of all mammals.
   Ⓒ Whales are largest than fish.
   Ⓓ Whales are large than sharks.

5. How many adjectives are in this sentence?
   We will have less money but more time if we take this train.
   Ⓐ one
   ● two
   Ⓒ three
   Ⓓ four

30 Adjectives: Review 2
Language Fundamentals • EMC 2754 • © Evan-Moor Corp.

Page 31

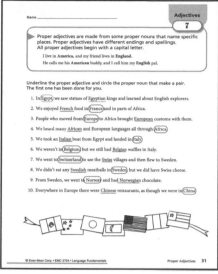

Name _____

Adjectives
7

Proper adjectives are made from some proper nouns that name specific places. Proper adjectives have different endings and spellings. All proper adjectives begin with a capital letter.

I live in **America**, and my friend lives in **England**.
He calls me his **American** buddy, and I call him my **English** pal.

Underline the proper adjective and circle the proper noun that make a pair.
The first one has been done for you.

1. In (Egypt) we saw statues of <u>Egyptian</u> kings and learned about English explorers.
2. We enjoyed <u>French</u> food in (France) and in parts of Africa.
3. People who moved from (Europe) to Africa brought <u>European</u> customs with them.
4. We heard many <u>African</u> and European languages all through (Africa).
5. We took an <u>Italian</u> boat from Egypt and landed in (Italy).
6. We weren't in (Belgium) but we still had <u>Belgian</u> waffles in Italy.
7. We went to (Switzerland) to see the <u>Swiss</u> villages and then flew to Sweden.
8. We didn't eat any <u>Swedish</u> meatballs in (Sweden), but we did have Swiss cheese.
9. From Sweden, we went to (Norway) and had <u>Norwegian</u> chocolate.
10. Everywhere in Europe were <u>Chinese</u> restaurants, as though we were in (China).

© Evan-Moor Corp. • EMC 2754 • Language Fundamentals
Proper Adjectives 31

Page 32

Name _____

Adjectives
8

Some proper adjectives are made from proper nouns that name specific places.

• Proper adjectives begin with a capital letter. Many proper adjectives end in -ese, -ian, -ish, or -ean.

ese	ian	ish	ean
Chinese	Egyptian	Irish	Chilean
Portuguese	Brazilian	Spanish	European
Vietnamese	Russian	Swedish	Korean

• Others have spellings different from the proper noun.

French Greek Swiss

Complete each sentence with the proper adjective made from the proper noun given.

1. The **European** Union is made up of 25 member countries.
   (Europe)
2. The **French** Resistance during World War II was famous.
   (France)
3. **Greek** mythology is filled with adventure.
   (Greece)
4. The **Chinese** New Year is celebrated for fifteen days.
   (China)
5. The samba is a **Brazilian** dance.
   (Brazil)
6. **Spanish** explorers charted much of the Americas.
   (Spain)
7. The **Egyptian** pyramids are one of the Seven Wonders of the World.
   (Egypt)
8. **Swiss** chalets are located high in the Alps.
   (Switzerland)

32 Proper Adjectives
Language Fundamentals • EMC 2754 • © Evan-Moor Corp.

Page 33

Name _____

Adjectives
Review 3

Fill in the bubble next to the correct answer.

1. Which underlined word is a proper adjective?
   Ⓐ <u>Paris</u> has lots of great museums.
   ● I met a <u>Parisian</u> woman on the train.
   Ⓒ We did not have time to see <u>Italy</u>.
   Ⓓ I will visit <u>Rome</u> on the next trip.

2. Which proper noun belongs with the underlined proper adjective?
   The <u>Iraqi</u> civilization is very old.
   Ⓐ Iran
   ● Iraq
   Ⓒ India
   Ⓓ Ireland

3. Which sentence correctly names a proper adjective?
   ● Many students in our class have Russian relatives.
   Ⓑ One student has grandparents who are Rushish.
   Ⓒ There are several students who come from Russia.
   Ⓓ They speak the language of Russia.

4. Which sentence correctly names the proper noun and proper adjective?
   Ⓐ We ate some Chilean food.
   Ⓑ Chile is a beautiful country!
   Ⓒ We had to get some Chilese dollars before we left for Chile.
   ● We saw fascinating Chilean cities on our travels in Chile.

5. Which word is <u>not</u> the correct proper adjective for a country?
   Ⓐ Portuguese
   ● Vietnamian
   Ⓒ Irish
   Ⓓ French

© Evan-Moor Corp. • EMC 2754 • Language Fundamentals
Adjectives: Review 3 33

Page 34

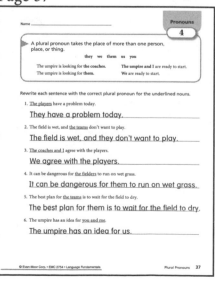

Name _____

Pronouns
1

A pronoun is a word used in place of a noun.

I you he she it they we me you him her it them us

Jacob has the games. **Emily and Olivia** have the food.
He has the games. **They** have the food.

Sonjay will meet **Ethan and Ryan. Aki** will come with **Madison and me.**
Sonjay will meet **them. She** will come with **us.**

Replace the underlined nouns with the correct pronouns.

1. <u>Daniel and I</u> are taking a train trip.
   We are taking a train trip.
2. I have traveled alone, but <u>Daniel</u> has not.
   I have traveled alone, but **he** has not.
3. <u>Mom and Dad</u> are working and cannot visit <u>our grandparents</u>.
   They are working and cannot visit **them**.
4. <u>Mom</u> says <u>the train</u> is the best way to go.
   She says **it** is the best way to go.
5. I'm bringing games and snacks for <u>Daniel and me</u>.
   I'm bringing games and snacks for **us**.
6. I am glad to be going with <u>Daniel</u>.
   I am glad to be going with **him**.

34 Identifying Pronouns
Language Fundamentals • EMC 2754 • © Evan-Moor Corp.

Page 35

Name _____

Pronouns
2

A pronoun is used in place of a noun.

I me you he she him her it they them we us

• Use pronouns to avoid repeating the same names in a sentence.

Joshua is meeting Caleb and David, and **Joshua** is late.
Joshua is meeting Caleb and David, and **he** is late.

• Use pronouns to avoid repeating the same words in a group of sentences.

The shells I found on the beach are in my suitcase. **The shells** are pink and white. **The shells** will go in my collection.
The shells I found on the beach are in my suitcase. **They** are pink and white. **They** will go in my collection.

Read the paragraphs. Replace the underlined words with the correct pronouns. Write the pronouns above the words.

Ashley is getting a new bike. <u>The bike</u> [It] is the first new bike for <u>Ashley</u> [her] in four years. <u>Mom</u> [She] pretended not to listen to <u>Ashley</u> when Ashley asked for a new bike. <u>Mom</u> knew that <u>a bike</u> [it] would make a great birthday present.

Mom and I went to pick out the bike. <u>Mom and I</u> [We] looked at all of the <u>bikes</u> [them]. Mr. Brown, the store manager, told <u>Mom and me</u> [us] that orange is a popular color. <u>Mom and I</u> [We] decided that Ashley would like an orange bike. Mom paid <u>Mr. Brown</u> [him] for <u>the orange bike</u> [it]. <u>Mr. Brown</u> [He] carried the orange <u>bike</u> [it] to the car. Now all <u>Mom and I</u> [we] have to do is wait for Ashley's birthday. <u>Ashley</u> [She] will be surprised!

© Evan-Moor Corp. • EMC 2754 • Language Fundamentals
Identifying Pronouns 35

Page 36

Name _____

Pronouns
3

A singular pronoun takes the place of one person, place, or thing.

I you he she it me him her

The tornado is dangerous.   The tornado surprised **the weatherman.**
It is dangerous.   The tornado surprised **him.**

Replace each underlined noun with the correct singular pronoun.

1. <u>Mrs. Ray</u> heard the storm warning on the radio.
   She heard the storm warning on the radio.
2. Mrs. Ray called <u>Selena</u> for help.
   Mrs. Ray called **her** for help.
3. <u>Selena</u> brought <u>Jared</u> to have an extra pair of hands.
   She brought **him** to have an extra pair of hands.
4. <u>Jared</u> told <u>Mrs. Ray</u> to go down to the basement.
   He told **her** to go down to the basement.
5. <u>The dog</u> is the main thing <u>Mrs. Ray</u> is worried about.
   It is the main thing **she** is worried about.
6. When <u>Jared</u> brought <u>the dog</u> to the basement, <u>Mrs. Ray</u> gave Jared a big hug!
   When **he** brought **it** to the basement, **she** gave **him** a big hug!

36 Singular Pronouns
Language Fundamentals • EMC 2754 • © Evan-Moor Corp.

Page 37

Name _____

Pronouns
4

A plural pronoun takes the place of more than one person, place, or thing.

they we them us you

The umpire is looking for the **coaches.**   **The umpire and I** are ready to start.
The umpire is looking for **them.**   **We** are ready to start.

Rewrite each sentence with the correct plural pronoun for the underlined nouns.

1. <u>The players</u> have a problem today.
   They have a problem today.
2. <u>The field</u> is wet, and <u>the teams</u> don't want to play.
   The field is wet, and they don't want to play.
3. <u>The coaches and I</u> agree with the players.
   We agree with the players.
4. It can be dangerous for <u>the fielders</u> to run on wet grass.
   It can be dangerous for them to run on wet grass.
5. The best plan for <u>the teams</u> is to wait for the field to dry.
   The best plan for them is to wait for the field to dry.
6. The umpire has an idea for <u>you and me</u>.
   The umpire has an idea for us.

© Evan-Moor Corp. • EMC 2754 • Language Fundamentals
Plural Pronouns 37

© Evan-Moor Corp. • EMC 2754 • Language Fundamentals

217

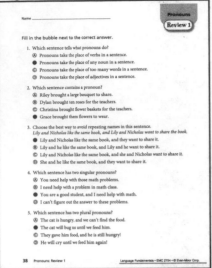

Pronouns — Review 1

Fill in the bubble next to the correct answer.

1. Which sentence tells what pronouns do?
Ⓐ Pronouns take the place of verbs in a sentence.
● Pronouns take the place of any noun in a sentence.
Ⓒ Pronouns take the place of too many words in a sentence.
Ⓓ Pronouns take the place of adjectives in a sentence.

2. Which sentence contains a pronoun?
Ⓐ Riley brought a large bouquet to share.
● Dylan brought ten roses for the teachers.
Ⓒ Christina brought flower baskets for the teachers.
Ⓓ Grace brought them flowers to wear.

3. Choose the best way to avoid repeating names in this sentence.
Lily and Nicholas like the same book, and Lily and Nicholas want to share the book.
● Lily and Nicholas like the same book, and they want to share it.
Ⓑ Lily and he like the same book, and Lily and he want to share it.
Ⓒ Lily and Nicholas like the same book, and she and Nicholas want to share it.
Ⓓ She and he like the same book, and they want to share it.

4. Which sentence has two singular pronouns?
Ⓐ You need help with those math problems.
● I need help with a problem in math class.
Ⓒ You are a good student, and I need help with math.
Ⓓ I can't figure out the answer to these problems.

5. Which sentence has two plural pronouns?
Ⓐ The cat is hungry, and we can't find the food.
● The cat will bug us until we feed him.
Ⓒ They gave him food, and he is still hungry!
Ⓓ He will cry until we feed him again!

38   Pronouns: Review 1 · Language Fundamentals · EMC 2754 · © Evan-Moor Corp.

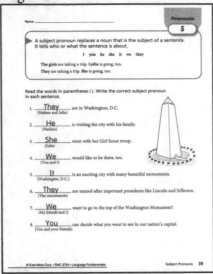

Pronouns 5

A subject pronoun replaces a noun that is the subject of a sentence. It tells who or what the sentence is about.

I   you   he   she   it   we   they

The girls are taking a trip. **Lydia** is going, too.
They are taking a trip. **She** is going, too.

Read the words in parentheses ( ). Write the correct subject pronoun in each sentence.

1. **They** (Nathan and Julia) are in Washington, D.C.
2. **He** (Nathan) is visiting the city with his family.
3. **She** (Julia) went with her Girl Scout troop.
4. **We** (You and I) would like to be there, too.
5. **It** (Washington, D.C.) is an exciting city with many beautiful monuments.
6. **They** (The monuments) are named after important presidents like Lincoln and Jefferson.
7. **We** (My friends and I) want to go to the top of the Washington Monument.
8. **You** (You and your friends) can decide what you want to see in our nation's capital.

© Evan-Moor Corp. · EMC 2754 · Language Fundamentals   Subject Pronouns   39

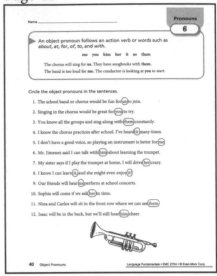

Pronouns 6

An object pronoun follows an action verb or words such as *about, at, for, of, to,* and *with.*

me   you   him   her   us   them

The chorus will sing for us. They have songbooks with them.
The band is too loud for me. The conductor is looking at you to start.

Circle the object pronouns in the sentences.

1. The school band or chorus would be fun for (us) to join.
2. Singing in the chorus would be great for (you) to try.
3. You know all the groups and sing along with (them) constantly.
4. I know the chorus practices after school. I've heard (it) many times.
5. I don't have a good voice, so playing an instrument is better for (me).
6. Mr. Jimenez said I can talk with (him) about learning the trumpet.
7. My sister says if I play the trumpet at home, I will drive (her) crazy.
8. I know I can learn (it), and she might even enjoy (it)!
9. Our friends will hear (us) perform at school concerts.
10. Sophia will come if we ask (her) in time.
11. Nina and Carlos will sit in the front row where we can see (them).
12. Isaac will be in the back, but we'll still hear (him) cheer.

40   Object Pronouns   Language Fundamentals · EMC 2754 · © Evan-Moor Corp.

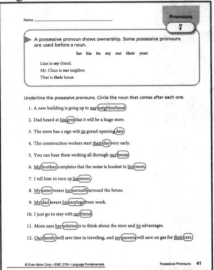

Pronouns 7

A possessive pronoun shows ownership. Some possessive pronouns are used before a noun.

her   his   its   my   our   their   your

Lian is **my** friend.
Mr. Chan is **our** neighbor.
That is **their** house.

Underline the possessive pronouns. Circle the noun that comes after each one.

1. A new building is going up in our (neighborhood).
2. Dad heard at his (gym) that it will be a huge store.
3. The store has a sign with its grand opening (date).
4. The construction workers start their (day) very early.
5. You can hear them working all through our (house).
6. My (brother) complains that the noise is loudest in his (room).
7. I tell him to turn up his (stereo).
8. My (sister) wears her (earmuffs) around the house.
9. My (dad) wears his (earplugs) from work.
10. I just go to stay with my (friend).
11. Mom says her (solution) is to think about the store and its (advantages).
12. Our (family) will save time in traveling, and my (parents) will save on gas for their (cars).

© Evan-Moor Corp. · EMC 2754 · Language Fundamentals   Possessive Pronouns   41

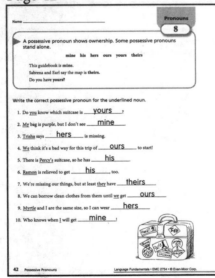

Pronouns 8

A possessive pronoun shows ownership. Some possessive pronouns stand alone.

mine   his   hers   ours   yours   theirs

This guidebook is **mine.**
Sabrena and Earl say the map is **theirs.**
Do you have **yours?**

Write the correct possessive pronoun for the underlined noun.

1. Do you know which suitcase is **yours**?
2. My bag is purple, but I don't see **mine**.
3. Trisha says **hers** is missing.
4. We think it's a bad way for this trip of **ours** to start!
5. There is Percy's suitcase, so he has **his**.
6. Ramon is relieved to get **his**, too.
7. We're missing our things, but at least they have **theirs**.
8. We can borrow clean clothes from them until we get **ours**.
9. Myrtle and I are the same size, so I can wear **hers**.
10. Who knows when I will get **mine**?

42   Possessive Pronouns   Language Fundamentals · EMC 2754 · © Evan-Moor Corp.

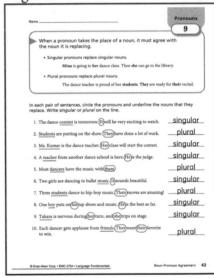

Pronouns 9

When a pronoun takes the place of a noun, it must agree with the noun it is replacing.

• Singular pronouns replace singular nouns.
  Mina is going to **her** dance class. Then **she** can go to the library.

• Plural pronouns replace plural nouns.
  The dance teacher is proud of her **students. They** are ready for **their** recital.

In each pair of sentences, circle the pronouns and underline the nouns that they replace. Write *singular* or *plural* on the line.

1. The dance (contest) is tomorrow. (It) will be very exciting to watch.   **singular**
2. (Students) are putting on the show. (They) have done a lot of work.   **plural**
3. Ms. (Kumar) is the dance teacher. (Her) class will start the contest.   **singular**
4. A (teacher) from another dance school is here. (He) is the judge.   **singular**
5. Most (dancers) have the music with (them).   **plural**
6. Two girls are dancing to ballet (music). (It) sounds beautiful.   **singular**
7. Three (students) dance to hip-hop music. (Their) moves are amazing!   **plural**
8. One (boy) puts on (his) tap shoes and music. (He) is the best so far.   **singular**
9. (Takara) is nervous during (her) turn, and (she) trips on stage.   **singular**
10. Each dancer gets applause from (friends). (They) want (their) favorite to win.   **plural**

© Evan-Moor Corp. · EMC 2754 · Language Fundamentals   Noun-Pronoun Agreement   43

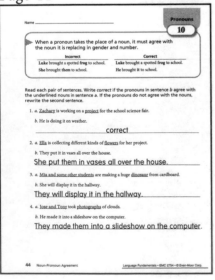

Pronouns 10

When a pronoun takes the place of a noun, it must agree with the noun it is replacing in gender and number.

Incorrect	Correct
Luke brought a spotted frog to school.	Luke brought a spotted frog to school.
She brought them to school.	He brought it to school.

Read each pair of sentences. Write *correct* if the pronouns in sentence *b* agree with the underlined nouns in sentence *a*. If the pronouns do not agree with the nouns, rewrite the second sentence.

1. a. Zachary is working on a project for the school science fair.
   b. He is doing it on weather.
   correct

2. a. Ella is collecting different kinds of flowers for her project.
   b. They put it in vases all over the house.
   She put them in vases all over the house.

3. a. Mia and some other students are making a huge dinosaur from cardboard.
   b. She will display it in the hallway.
   They will display it in the hallway.

4. a. Jose and Tony took photographs of clouds.
   b. He made it into a slideshow on the computer.
   They made them into a slideshow on the computer.

44   Noun-Pronoun Agreement   Language Fundamentals · EMC 2754 · © Evan-Moor Corp.

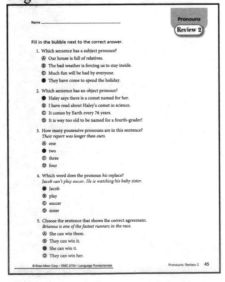

Pronouns — Review 2

Fill in the bubble next to the correct answer.

1. Which sentence has a subject pronoun?
● Our house is full of relatives.
Ⓑ The bad weather is forcing us to stay inside.
Ⓒ Much fun will be had by everyone.
Ⓓ They have come to spend the holiday.

2. Which sentence has an object pronoun?
● Haley says there is a comet named for her.
Ⓑ I have read about Haley's comet in science.
Ⓒ It comes by Earth every 76 years.
Ⓓ It is way too old to be named for a fourth-grader!

3. How many possessive pronouns are in this sentence?
Their report was longer than ours.
Ⓐ one
● two
Ⓒ three
Ⓓ four

4. Which word does the pronoun *his* replace?
Jacob can't play soccer. He is watching his baby sister.
● Jacob
Ⓑ play
Ⓒ soccer
Ⓓ sister

5. Choose the sentence that shows the correct agreement.
Brianna is one of the fastest runners in the race.
Ⓐ She can win them.
Ⓑ They can win it.
● She can win it.
Ⓓ They can win her.

© Evan-Moor Corp. · EMC 2754 · Language Fundamentals   Pronouns: Review 2   45

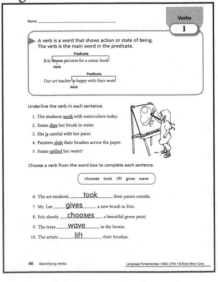

Verbs 1

A verb is a word that shows action or state of being. The verb is the main word in the predicate.

Predicate
Eric **draws** pictures for a comic book.
Verb

Predicate
Our art teacher **is** happy with their work.
Verb

Underline the verb in each sentence.

1. The students **work** with watercolors today.
2. Susan **dips** her brush in water.
3. She **is** careful with her paint.
4. Painters **slide** their brushes across the paper.
5. Susan **spilled** her water!

Choose a verb from the word box to complete each sentence.

chooses   took   lift   gives   wave

6. The art students **took** their paints outside.
7. Mr. Lee **gives** a new brush to Eric.
8. Eric slowly **chooses** a beautiful green paint.
9. The trees **wave** in the breeze.
10. The artists **lift** their brushes.

46   Identifying Verbs   Language Fundamentals · EMC 2754 · © Evan-Moor Corp.

Page 47

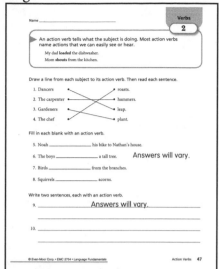

Verbs 2

An action verb tells what the subject is doing. Most action verbs name actions that we can easily see or hear.

My dad **loaded** the dishwasher.
Mom **shouts** from the kitchen.

Draw a line from each subject to its action verb. Then read each sentence.

1. Dancers — roasts.
2. The carpenter — hammers.
3. Gardeners — leap.
4. The chef — plant.

Fill in each blank with an action verb.

5. Noah _____ his bike to Nathan's house.
6. The boys _____ a tall tree.   **Answers will vary.**
7. Birds _____ from the branches.
8. Squirrels _____ acorns.

Write two sentences, each with an action verb.

9. _____ **Answers will vary.**
10. _____

Page 48

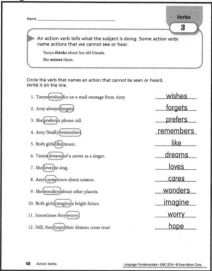

Verbs 3

An action verb tells what the subject is doing. Some action verbs name actions that we cannot see or hear.

Tanya **thinks** about her old friends.
She **misses** them.

Circle the verb that names an action that cannot be seen or heard. Write it on the line.

1. Tanya (wishes) for an e-mail message from Amy. _____ wishes
2. Amy always (forgets). _____ forgets
3. She (prefers) a phone call. _____ prefers
4. Amy finally (remembers). _____ remembers
5. Both girls (like) music. _____ like
6. Tanya (dreams) of a career as a singer. _____ dreams
7. She (loves) to sing. _____ loves
8. Amy (cares) more about science. _____ cares
9. She (wonders) about other planets. _____ wonders
10. Both girls (imagine) a bright future. _____ imagine
11. Sometimes they (worry). _____ worry
12. Still, they (hope) their dreams come true! _____ hope

Page 49

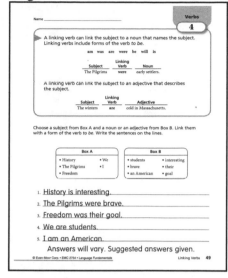

Verbs 4

A linking verb can link the subject to a noun that names the subject. Linking verbs include forms of the verb to be.

am was are were be will is

Subject	Linking Verb	Noun
The Pilgrims	were	early settlers.

A linking verb can link the subject to an adjective that describes the subject.

Subject	Linking Verb	Adjective
The winters	are	cold in Massachusetts.

Choose a subject from Box A and a noun or an adjective from Box B. Link them with a form of the verb to be. Write the sentences on the lines.

Box A
- History • We
- The Pilgrims • I
- Freedom

Box B
- students • interesting
- brave • their
- an American • goal

1. History is interesting.
2. The Pilgrims were brave.
3. Freedom was their goal.
4. We are students.
5. I am an American.

Answers will vary. Suggested answers given.

Page 50

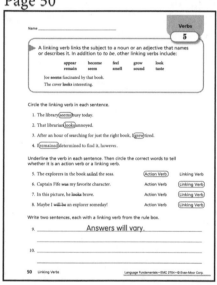

Verbs 5

A linking verb links the subject to a noun or an adjective that names or describes it. In addition to to be, other linking verbs include:

appear   become   feel   grow   look
remain   seem   smell   sound   taste

Joe **seems** fascinated by that book.
The cover **looks** interesting.

Circle the linking verb in each sentence.

1. The library (seems) busy today.
2. That librarian (looks) annoyed.
3. After an hour of searching for just the right book, I (grew) tired.
4. I (remained) determined to find it, however.

Underline the verb in each sentence. Then circle the correct words to tell whether it is an action verb or a linking verb.

5. The explorers in the book sailed the seas.   Action Verb / (Linking Verb)
6. Captain Fife was my favorite character.   Action Verb / (Linking Verb)
7. In this picture, he looks brave.   Action Verb / (Linking Verb)
8. Maybe I will be an explorer someday!   Action Verb / (Linking Verb)

Write two sentences, each with a linking verb from the rule box.

9. _____ **Answers will vary.**
10. _____

Page 51

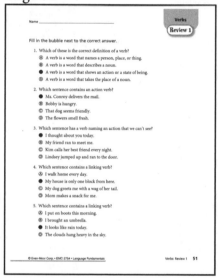

Verbs Review 1

Fill in the bubble next to the correct answer.

1. Which of these is the correct definition of a verb?
   Ⓐ A verb is a word that names a person, place, or thing.
   Ⓑ A verb is a word that describes a noun.
   ● A verb is a word that shows an action or a state of being.
   Ⓓ A verb is a word that takes the place of a noun.

2. Which sentence contains an action verb?
   ● Ms. Conroy delivers the mail.
   Ⓑ Bobby is hungry.
   Ⓒ That dog seems friendly.
   Ⓓ The flowers smell fresh.

3. Which sentence has a verb naming an action that we can't see?
   ● I thought about you today.
   Ⓑ My friend ran to meet me.
   Ⓒ Kim calls her best friend every night.
   Ⓓ Lindsey jumped up and ran to the door.

4. Which sentence contains a linking verb?
   Ⓐ I walk home every day.
   ● My house is only one block from here.
   Ⓒ My dog greets me with a wag of her tail.
   Ⓓ Mom makes a snack for me.

5. Which sentence contains a linking verb?
   Ⓐ I put on boots this morning.
   Ⓑ I brought an umbrella.
   ● It looks like rain today.
   Ⓓ The clouds hang heavy in the sky.

Page 52

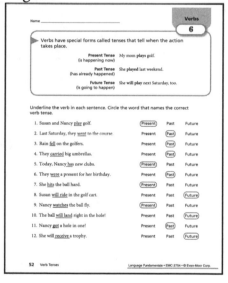

Verbs 6

Verbs have special forms called tenses that tell when the action takes place.

Present Tense (is happening now)   My mom **plays** golf.
Past Tense (has already happened)   She **played** last weekend.
Future Tense (is going to happen)   She **will play** next Saturday, too.

Underline the verb in each sentence. Circle the word that names the correct verb tense.

1. Susan and Nancy play golf.   (Present) Past Future
2. Last Saturday, they went to the course.   Present (Past) Future
3. Rain fell on the golfers.   Present (Past) Future
4. They carried big umbrellas.   Present (Past) Future
5. Today, Nancy has new clubs.   (Present) Past Future
6. They were a present for her birthday.   Present (Past) Future
7. She hits the ball hard.   (Present) Past Future
8. Susan will ride in the golf cart.   Present Past (Future)
9. Nancy watches the ball fly.   (Present) Past Future
10. The ball will land right in the hole!   Present Past (Future)
11. Nancy got a hole in one!   Present (Past) Future
12. She will receive a trophy.   Present Past (Future)

Page 53

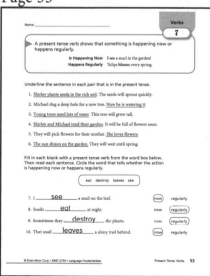

Verbs 7

A present tense verb shows that something is happening now or happens regularly.

Is Happening Now I **see** a snail in the garden!
Happens Regularly Tulips **bloom** every spring.

Underline the sentence in each pair that is in the present tense.

1. Shirley plants seeds in the rich soil. The seeds will sprout quickly.
2. Michael dug a deep hole for a new tree. Now he is watering it.
3. Young trees need lots of water. This tree will grow tall.
4. Shirley and Michael tend their garden. It will be full of flowers soon.
5. They will pick flowers for their mother. She loves flowers.
6. The sun shines on the garden. They will wait until spring.

Fill in each blank with a present tense verb from the word box below. Then read each sentence. Circle the word that tells whether the action is happening now or happens regularly.

eat   destroy   leaves   see

7. I _____ see _____ a snail on the leaf.   (now) regularly
8. Snails _____ eat _____ at night.   now (regularly)
9. Sometimes they _____ destroy _____ the plants.   now (regularly)
10. That snail _____ leaves _____ a slimy trail behind.   (now) regularly

Page 54

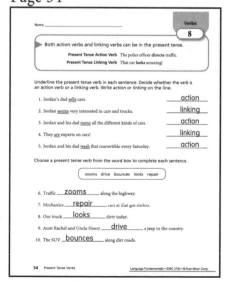

Verbs 8

Both action verbs and linking verbs can be in the present tense.

Present Tense Action Verb The police officer **directs** traffic.
Present Tense Linking Verb That car **looks** amazing!

Underline the present tense verb in each sentence. Decide whether the verb is an action verb or a linking verb. Write action or linking on the line.

1. Jordan's dad sells cars. _____ action
2. Jordan seems very interested in cars and trucks. _____ linking
3. Jordan and his dad name all the different kinds of cars. _____ action
4. They are experts on cars! _____ linking
5. Jordan and his dad wash that convertible every Saturday. _____ action

Choose a present tense verb from the word box to complete each sentence.

zooms   drive   bounces   looks   repair

6. Traffic _____ zooms _____ along the highway.
7. Mechanics _____ repair _____ cars at that gas station.
8. Our truck _____ looks _____ dirty today.
9. Aunt Rachel and Uncle Henry _____ drive _____ a jeep in the country.
10. The SUV _____ bounces _____ along dirt roads.

Page 55

Verbs 9

A past tense verb tells about something that happened in the past and is over.

My family **traveled** to France last year.
My grandfather once **studied** in Paris.
He **was** an art student.

Underline the sentence that tells about something that has happened or was in the past. Circle the past tense verb.

1. Paris is the capital city of France. My grandfather (lived) there for a year.
2. My grandfather works in advertising. In Paris, he (took) art classes.
3. My family (went) to France on vacation. I remember everything about our trip.
4. I have a photo album full of pictures. I (took) a dozen pictures of the Eiffel Tower.
5. Gustave Eiffel (designed) the tower in the year 1889. It is tall and beautiful.

Write three sentences about a place that you have visited. Use a past tense verb in each sentence.

6. _____ **Answers will vary.**
7. _____
8. _____

Page 56

Name _____

The past tense of most verbs is formed by adding *ed*. The verbs that follow this rule are called regular verbs.

Present Tense We **play** basketball on Saturdays.
Past Tense We **played** for an hour last week.

Write the past tense of these regular verbs.

1. walk — **walked**
2. wash — **washed**
3. cook — **cooked**
4. open — **opened**
5. laugh — **laughed**
6. call — **called**
7. tramp — **tramped**
8. turn — **turned**

Write each sentence in the past tense.

9. The players pass the ball back and forth.
The players passed the ball back and forth.

10. The fans shout from the stands.
The fans shouted from the stands.

11. I return the ball to the referee.
I returned the ball to the referee.

12. The fans roar with excitement!
The fans roared with excitement!

Page 57

Name _____

Some regular verbs require spelling changes before adding *ed* to form the past tense.

• When a verb ends in a silent *e*, drop the silent *e* and add *ed*.
move → moved   wave → waved   hope → hoped

• When a verb ends in a consonant followed by a *y*, change the *y* to *i* and add *ed*.
cry → cried   study → studied   hurry → hurried

• When a verb ends in a short vowel followed by a single consonant, double the final consonant and add *ed*.
hop → hopped   grab → grabbed   trim → trimmed

Complete each sentence with the past tense form of the verb in parentheses ( ).

1. Riley **named** his cat Domino.
(name)

2. Domino **tried** to catch a mouse in the kitchen.
(try)

3. Riley **chased** the mouse, too.
(chase)

4. The mouse **carried** a crust of bread as it ran.
(carry)

5. Riley **tripped** on his shoelace.
(trip)

6. Domino's whiskers **wiggled**.
(wiggle)

7. Riley **spied** the mouse behind the cookie jar.
(spy)

8. The little mouse **dropped** a cookie crumb.
(drop)

Page 58

Name _____

Some verbs do not follow a set rule to form the past tense. These verbs are called irregular verbs.

Present We **buy** groceries every week.   I **eat** breakfast in the kitchen.
Past We **bought** maple syrup for our pancakes.   Yesterday, I **ate** a bowl of cereal.

Complete each sentence with the correct past tense verb in parentheses ( ).

1. I **slept** late on Saturday.
(sleeped, slept)

2. My alarm clock **rang** at 7 o'clock.
(rang, ringed)

3. I **shut** off the annoying sound.
(shut, shutted)

4. I **fell** asleep again.
(falled, fell)

5. At 9 o'clock in the morning, I **rose**.
(rose, rised)

6. At last, I **swung** my feet to the floor.
(swung, swinged)

7. My feet **froze** on the cold floor.
(freezed, froze)

8. I **hid** under the covers again!
(hid, hided)

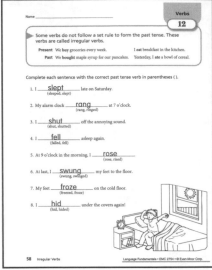

Page 59

Name _____

Verbs that do not follow a set rule to form the past tense are called irregular verbs. Many verbs that we use every day have an irregular past tense.

Present I go to the skating rink every week.   I always **buy** a snack there.
Past I **went** last just Thursday.   Last time, I **bought** an ice-cream bar.

Write the past tense form of each irregular verb.

Present	Irregular Past		Present	Irregular Past
1. ride	**rode**		9. fly	**flew**
2. come	**came**		10. begin	**began**
3. give	**gave**		11. see	**saw**
4. do	**did**		12. pay	**paid**
5. have	**had**		13. teach	**taught**
6. is	**was**		14. wear	**wore**
7. win	**won**		15. find	**found**
8. bring	**brought**		16. throw	**threw**

Write four sentences, each with an irregular past tense verb.

17. **Answers will vary.**
18. _____
19. _____
20. _____

Page 60

Name _____

Fill in the bubble next to the correct answer.

1. What does the verb tense tell us?
● The verb tense tells when the action takes place.
Ⓑ The verb tense tells where the action takes place.
Ⓒ The verb tense tells who is performing the action.
Ⓓ The verb tense tells us what the action is about.

2. Which sentence is in the present tense?
Ⓐ Willie turned on the lights.
Ⓑ Sam sat in his desk.
● Paula talks to the teacher.
Ⓓ Kayla was late today.

3. What does the past tense of a verb show?
Ⓐ The past tense shows that the action is taking place now.
● The past tense shows that the action took place before now and is over.
Ⓒ The past tense shows that the action has not yet taken place.
Ⓓ The past tense shows that the action might take place.

4. Which of these is the past tense of the verb *tap*?
Ⓐ taped
Ⓑ tapt
Ⓒ tappet
● tapped

5. Which of these is the past tense of the verb *cry*?
Ⓐ cryed
Ⓑ cride
Ⓒ criied
● cried

Page 61

Name _____

Helping verbs come before the main verb. They help the main verb show time or tell more about the action.

am	was	being	does	has	might	should
are	were	been	did	had	can	would
is	be	do	have	may	could	will

Mr. Richards **has** chosen the actors for the play.
I **had** hoped to get a part.
I **am** helping with the sets and costumes instead.

Circle the helping verb and underline the main verb in each sentence.

1. The play (was) written by a famous author.
2. I (am) reading the first act now.
3. Leslie (has) walked onto the stage.
4. She (was) given the biggest part in the play.
5. Bob (might) build the sets with me.

Fill in each blank with the correct helping verb from the word box below. Then read the sentences.

is   might   has   are   am

6. Bob and I **are** pounding nails into the set.
7. I **am** working hard.
8. Leslie **is** practicing her first speech.
9. Mr. Richards **has** told her to speak louder.
10. The play **might** be a big hit!

Page 62

Name _____

A helping verb helps the main verb state the action or show time. In questions, the subject comes between the helping verb and the main verb.

Are you **going** on the field trip?
Will the blacksmith **make** a horseshoe?
Has the bus **arrived** yet?

Circle the helping verb and underline the main verb in each question.

1. (Is) the bus taking us to the historic village today?
2. (Will) Ms. Kampo tell us about life in the olden days?
3. (Can) you see the blacksmith?
4. (Is) the hammering a horseshoe?

Unscramble each set of words to form a question and write it on the line. Circle the helping verb.

5. eating barn cows are in the
(Are) cows eating in the barn?

6. the villagers grind did wheat
(Did) the villagers grind wheat?

7. a make does flour mill
(Does) a mill make flour?

8. you do smell cookies bakery's
(Do) you smell the bakery's cookies?

Page 63

Name _____

A future tense verb tells that an action or state of being has not begun yet, but is going to happen. Use the helping verb *will* with a main verb to form the future tense.

The animal shelter **holds** an open house. The animal shelter **will hold** an open house.
Jane **adopts** a pet rabbit. Jane **will adopt** a pet rabbit.

Complete each sentence with the future tense of the verb in parentheses ( ).

1. Many kittens **will be** ready for adoption from the shelter.
(be)

2. Jane **will look** for a rabbit.
(look)

3. A pet rabbit **will chew** on almost anything!
(chew)

Rewrite each sentence in the future tense.

4. My brothers walk the dog.
My brothers will walk the dog.

5. I feed our new kitten.
I will feed our new kitten.

6. Jane names her rabbit Flopsy.
Jane will name her rabbit Flopsy.

7. Jane's mom buys a comfortable cage for the rabbit.
Jane's mom will buy a comfortable cage for the rabbit.

8. That bunny makes a lovely pet!
That bunny will make a lovely pet!

Page 64

Name _____

Future tense verbs tell that an action or state of being has not begun yet, but is going to happen. Use the helping verb *will* with a main verb to form the future tense.

The neighbors **will have** a barbeque on Saturday.
Everyone **will eat** hamburgers and hot dogs.
I **will go** to a dinner party instead.

Answers will vary; possible answers are indicated.

Complete each sentence with a future tense verb.

1. The Gibbs family **will invite/have** neighbors over for an outdoor party.
2. Mr. Gibbs **will cook/grill/roast** hamburgers and hot dogs on the grill.
3. Jimmy **will mix/make** his special lemonade.
4. The neighborhood kids **will play/enjoy** games in the backyard.
5. Mrs. Gibbs **will teach/show** us how to play lawn tennis.
6. After supper, everyone **will roast/toast** marshmallows over the coals.
7. Maybe we **will catch/see** fireflies.

Write three sentences in the future tense about what you will do after school today.

8. **Answers will vary.**
9. _____
10. _____

Page 65

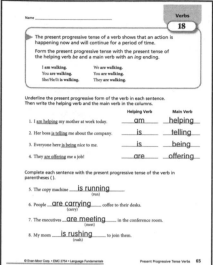

Verbs 18

The present progressive tense of a verb shows that an action is happening now and will continue for a period of time.

Form the present progressive tense with the present tense of the helping verb *be* and a main verb with an *ing* ending.

I am walking.	We are walking.
You are walking.	You are walking.
She/He/It is walking.	They are walking.

Underline the present progressive form of the verb in each sentence. Then write the helping verb and the main verb in the columns.

	Helping Verb	Main Verb
1. I <u>am helping</u> my mother at work today.	am	helping
2. Her boss <u>is telling</u> me about the company.	is	telling
3. Everyone here <u>is being</u> nice to me.	is	being
4. They <u>are offering</u> me a job!	are	offering

Complete each sentence with the present progressive tense of the verb in parentheses ( ).

5. The copy machine **is running** (run)

6. People **are carrying** coffee to their desks. (carry)

7. The executives **are meeting** in the conference room. (meet)

8. My mom **is rushing** to join them. (rush)

Present Progressive Tense Verbs 65

Page 66

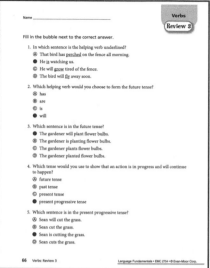

Verbs Review 3

Fill in the bubble next to the correct answer.

1. In which sentence is the helping verb underlined?
   - Ⓐ That bird has <u>perched</u> on the fence all morning.
   - ● He is <u>watching</u> us.
   - Ⓒ He will <u>grow</u> tired of the fence.
   - Ⓓ The bird will <u>fly</u> away soon.

2. Which helping verb would you choose to form the future tense?
   - Ⓐ has
   - Ⓑ are
   - Ⓒ is
   - ● will

3. Which sentence is in the future tense?
   - ● The gardener will plant flower bulbs.
   - Ⓑ The gardener is planting flower bulbs.
   - Ⓒ The gardener plants flower bulbs.
   - Ⓓ The gardener planted flower bulbs.

4. Which tense would you use to show that an action is in progress and will continue to happen?
   - Ⓐ future tense
   - Ⓑ past tense
   - Ⓒ present tense
   - ● present progressive tense

5. Which sentence is in the present progressive tense?
   - Ⓐ Sean will cut the grass.
   - Ⓑ Sean cut the grass.
   - ● Sean is cutting the grass.
   - Ⓓ Sean cuts the grass.

66 Verbs: Review 3

Page 67

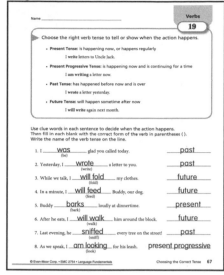

Verbs 19

Choose the right verb tense to tell or show when the action happens.

- **Present Tense:** is happening now, or happens regularly

   I write letters to Uncle Jack.

- **Present Progressive Tense:** is happening now and is continuing for a time

   I am writing a letter now.

- **Past Tense:** has happened before now and is over

   I wrote a letter yesterday.

- **Future Tense:** will happen sometime after now

   I will write again next month.

Use clue words in each sentence to decide when the action happens. Then fill in each blank with the correct form of the verb in parentheses ( ). Write the name of the verb tense on the line.

1. I **was** glad you called today. (be) — **past**

2. Yesterday, I **wrote** a letter to you. (write) — **past**

3. While we talk, I **will fold** my clothes. (fold) — **future**

4. In a minute, I **will feed** Buddy, our dog. (feed) — **future**

5. Buddy **barks** loudly at dinnertime. (bark) — **present**

6. After he eats, I **will walk** him around the block. (walk) — **future**

7. Last evening, he **sniffed** every tree on the street! (sniff) — **past**

8. As we speak, I **am looking** for his leash. (look) — **present progressive**

Choosing the Correct Tense 67

Page 68

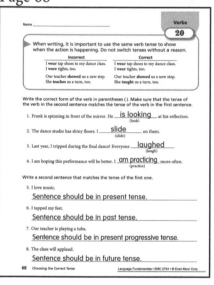

Verbs 20

When writing, it is important to use the same verb tense to show when the action is happening. Do not switch tenses without a reason.

Incorrect	Correct
I **wear** tap shoes to my dance class.	I **wear** tap shoes to my dance class.
I **wore** tights, too.	I **wear** tights, too.
Our teacher **showed** us a new step.	Our teacher **showed** us a new step.
She **teaches** us a turn, too.	She **taught** us a turn, too.

Write the correct form of the verb in parentheses ( ). Make sure that the tense of the verb in the second sentence matches the tense of the verb in the first sentence.

1. Frank is spinning in front of the mirror. He **is looking** at his reflection. (look)

2. The dance studio has shiny floors. I **slide** on them. (slide)

3. Last year, I tripped during the final dance! Everyone **laughed** (laugh)

4. I am hoping this performance will be better. I **am practicing** more often. (practice)

Write a second sentence that matches the tense of the first one.

5. I love music.
   Sentence should be in present tense.

6. I tapped my feet.
   Sentence should be in past tense.

7. Our teacher is playing a tuba.
   Sentence should be in present progressive tense.

8. The class will applaud.
   Sentence should be in future tense.

68 Choosing the Correct Tense

Page 69

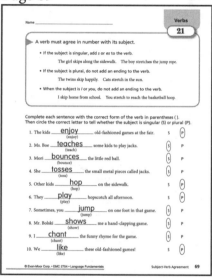

Verbs 21

A verb must agree in number with its subject.

- If the subject is singular, add *s* or *es* to the verb.

   The girl skips along the sidewalk.   The boy stretches the jump rope.

- If the subject is plural, do not add an ending to the verb.

   The twins skip happily.   Cats stretch in the sun.

- When the subject is I or you, do not add an ending to the verb.

   I skip home from school.   You stretch to reach the basketball hoop.

Complete each sentence with the correct form of the verb in parentheses ( ). Then circle the correct letter to tell whether the subject is singular (S) or plural (P).

1. The kids **enjoy** old-fashioned games at the fair. (enjoy) — S ⓟ

2. Ms. Boe **teaches** some kids to play jacks. (teach) — Ⓢ P

3. Mori **bounces** the little red ball. (bounce) — Ⓢ P

4. She **tosses** the small metal pieces called jacks. (toss) — Ⓢ P

5. Other kids **hop** on the sidewalk. (hop) — S ⓟ

6. They **play** hopscotch all afternoon. (play) — S ⓟ

7. Sometimes, you **jump** on one foot in that game. (jump) — Ⓢ P

8. Mr. Bolski **shows** me a hand-clapping game. (show) — Ⓢ P

9. I **chant** the funny rhyme for the game. (chant) — Ⓢ P

10. We **like** these old-fashioned games! (like) — S ⓟ

Subject-Verb Agreement 69

Page 70

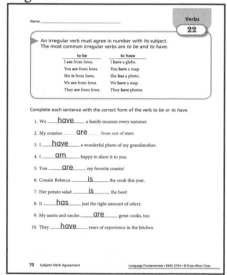

Verbs 22

An irregular verb must agree in number with its subject. The most common irregular verbs are *to be* and *to have*.

to be	to have
I am from Iowa.	I have a globe.
You are from Iowa.	You have a map.
She is from Iowa.	She has a photo.
We are from Iowa.	We have a map.
They are from Iowa.	They have photos.

Complete each sentence with the correct form of the verb *to be* or *to have*.

1. We **have** a family reunion every summer.

2. My cousins **are** from out of state.

3. I **have** a wonderful photo of my grandmother.

4. I **am** happy to show it to you.

5. You **are** my favorite cousin!

6. Cousin Rebecca **is** the cook this year.

7. Her potato salad **is** the best!

8. It **has** just the right amount of celery.

9. My aunts and uncles **are** great cooks, too.

10. They **have** years of experience in the kitchen.

70 Subject-Verb Agreement

Page 71

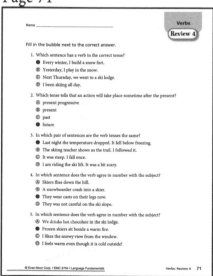

Verbs Review 4

Fill in the bubble next to the correct answer.

1. Which sentence has a verb in the correct tense?
   - ● Every winter, I build a snow fort.
   - Ⓑ Yesterday, I play in the snow.
   - Ⓒ Next Thursday, we went to a ski lodge.
   - Ⓓ I been skiing all day.

2. Which tense tells that an action will take place sometime after the present?
   - Ⓐ present progressive
   - Ⓑ present
   - Ⓒ past
   - ● future

3. In which pair of sentences are the verb tenses the same?
   - ● Last night the temperature dropped. It fell below freezing.
   - Ⓑ The skiing teacher shows us the trail. I followed it.
   - Ⓒ It was steep. I fall once.
   - Ⓓ I am riding the ski lift. It was a bit scary.

4. In which sentence does the verb agree in number with the subject?
   - Ⓐ Skiers flies down the hill.
   - Ⓑ A snowboarder crash into a skier.
   - ● They wear casts on their legs now.
   - Ⓓ They was not careful on the ski slope.

5. In which sentence does the verb agree in number with the subject?
   - Ⓐ We drinks hot chocolate in the ski lodge.
   - ● Frozen skiers sit beside a warm fire.
   - Ⓒ I likes the snowy view from the window.
   - Ⓓ I feels warm even though it is cold outside!

Verbs: Review 4 71

Page 72

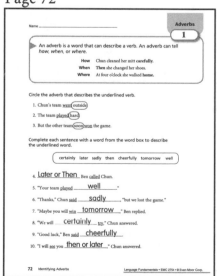

Adverbs 1

An adverb is a word that can describe a verb. An adverb can tell *how*, *when*, or *where*.

How	Chun cleaned her mitt **carefully**.
When	**Then** she changed her shoes.
Where	At four o'clock she walked **home**.

Circle the adverb that describes the underlined verb.

1. Chun's team <u>went</u> (outside)

2. The team <u>played</u> (hard)

3. But the other team (soon)<u>won</u> the game.

Complete each sentence with a word from the word box to describe the underlined word.

> certainly   later   sadly   then   cheerfully   tomorrow   well

4. **Later or Then** Ben <u>called</u> Chun.

5. "Your team <u>played</u> **well**."

6. "Thanks," Chun <u>said</u> **sadly**, "but we lost the game."

7. "Maybe you will <u>win</u> **tomorrow**," Ben replied.

8. "We will **certainly** <u>try</u>," Chun answered.

9. "Good luck," Ben <u>said</u> **cheerfully**.

10. "I will <u>see</u> you **then or later**," Chun answered.

72 Identifying Adverbs

Page 73

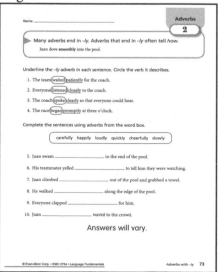

Adverbs 2

Many adverbs end in *–ly*. Adverbs that end in *–ly* often tell *how*.

Juan dove **smoothly** into the pool.

Underline the *–ly* adverb in each sentence. Circle the verb it describes.

1. The team (waited) <u>patiently</u> for the coach.

2. Everyone (listened) <u>closely</u> to the coach.

3. The coach (spoke) <u>clearly</u> so that everyone could hear.

4. The race (began) <u>promptly</u> at three o'clock.

Complete the sentences using adverbs from the word box.

> carefully   happily   loudly   quickly   cheerfully   slowly

5. Juan swam _____ to the end of the pool.

6. His teammates yelled _____ to tell him they were watching.

7. Juan climbed _____ out of the pool and grabbed a towel.

8. He walked _____ along the edge of the pool.

9. Everyone clapped _____ for him.

10. Juan _____ waved to the crowd.

Answers will vary.

Adverbs with *–ly* 73

Page 74

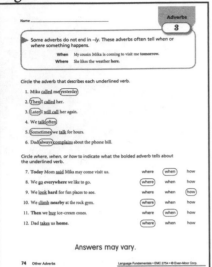

Some adverbs do not end in –ly. These adverbs often tell *when* or *where* something happens.

When My cousin Mika is coming to visit me **tomorrow**.
Where She likes the weather **here**.

Circle the adverb that describes each underlined verb.

1. Mika called me (yesterday)
2. (Then) I called her.
3. (Later) I will call her again.
4. We talk (often)
5. (Sometimes) we talk for hours.
6. Dad (always) complains about the phone bill.

Circle *where*, *when*, or *how* to indicate what the bolded adverb tells about the underlined verb.

7. **Today** Mom said Mika may visit us. where (when) how
8. We go **everywhere** we like to go. (where) when how
9. We look hard for fun places to see. where when (how)
10. We climb **nearby** at the rock gym. (where) when how
11. **Then** we buy ice-cream cones. where (when) how
12. Dad takes us **home**. (where) when how

Answers may vary.

74 Other Adverbs Language Fundamentals • EMC 2754 • © Evan-Moor Corp.

Page 75

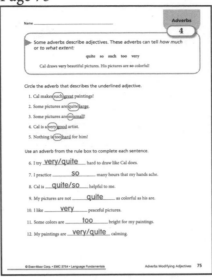

Some adverbs describe adjectives. These adverbs can tell *how much* or *to what extent*.

quite so such too very

Cal draws very beautiful pictures. His pictures are so colorful!

Circle the adverb that describes the underlined adjective.

1. Cal makes (such) great paintings!
2. Some pictures are (quite) large.
3. Some pictures are (so) small!
4. Cal is a (very) good artist.
5. Nothing is (too) hard for him!

Use an adverb from the rule box to complete each sentence.

6. I try __very/quite__ hard to draw like Cal does.
7. I practice __so__ many hours that my hands ache.
8. Cal is __quite/so__ helpful to me.
9. My pictures are not __quite__ as colorful as his are.
10. I like __very__ peaceful pictures.
11. Some colors are __too__ bright for my paintings.
12. My paintings are __very/quite__ calming.

© Evan-Moor Corp. • EMC 2754 • Language Fundamentals Adverbs Modifying Adjectives 75

Page 76

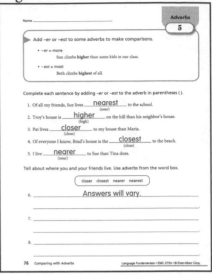

Add –er or –est to some adverbs to make comparisons.

• –er = more
   Sun climbs **higher** than some kids in our class.

• –est = most
   Beth climbs **highest** of all.

Complete each sentence by adding –er or –est to the adverb in parentheses ( ).

1. Of all my friends, Sue lives __nearest__ to the school.
   (near)
2. Troy's house is __higher__ on the hill than his neighbor's house.
   (high)
3. Pat lives __closer__ to my house than Maria.
   (close)
4. Of everyone I know, Brad's house is the __closest__ to the beach.
   (close)
5. I live __nearer__ to Sue than Tina does.
   (near)

Tell about where you and your friends live. Use adverbs from the word box.

closer closest nearer nearest

6. _____ Answers will vary. _____

7. _____

8. _____

76 Comparing with Adverbs Language Fundamentals • EMC 2754 • © Evan-Moor Corp.

Page 77

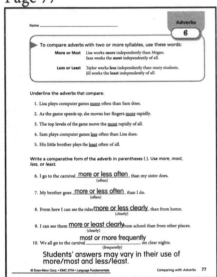

To compare adverbs with two or more syllables, use these words:

More or Most Lisa works **more** independently than Megan.
   Sam works the **most** independently of all.

Less or Least Taylor works **less** independently than many students.
   Jill works the **least** independently of all.

Underline the adverbs that compare.

1. Lisa plays computer games more often than Sam does.
2. As the game speeds up, she moves her fingers more rapidly.
3. The top levels of the game move the most rapidly of all.
4. Sam plays computer games less often than Lisa does.
5. His little brother plays the least often of all.

Write a comparative form of the adverb in parentheses ( ). Use *more, most, less*, or *least*.

6. I go to the carnival __more or less often__ than my sister does.
   (often)
7. My brother goes __more or less often__ than I do.
   (often)
8. From here I can see the rides __more or less clearly__ than from home.
   (clearly)
9. I can see them __more or least clearly__ from school than from other places.
   (clearly)
10. We all go to the carnival __most or more frequently__ on clear nights.
   (frequently)

Students' answers may vary in their use of more/most and less/least.

© Evan-Moor Corp. • EMC 2754 • Language Fundamentals Comparing with Adverbs 77

Page 78

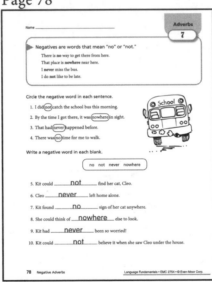

Negatives are words that mean "no" or "not."

There is **no** way to get there from here.
That place is **nowhere** near here.
I **never** miss the bus.
I do **not** like to be late.

Circle the negative word in each sentence.

1. I did (not) catch the school bus this morning.
2. By the time I got there, it was (nowhere) in sight.
3. That had (never) happened before.
4. There was (no) time for me to walk.

Write a negative word in each blank.

no not never nowhere

5. Kit could __not__ find her cat, Cleo.
6. Cleo __never__ left home alone.
7. Kit found __no__ sign of her cat anywhere.
8. She could think of __nowhere__ else to look.
9. Kit had __never__ been so worried!
10. Kit could __not__ believe it when she saw Cleo under the house.

78 Negative Adverbs Language Fundamentals • EMC 2754 • © Evan-Moor Corp.

Page 79

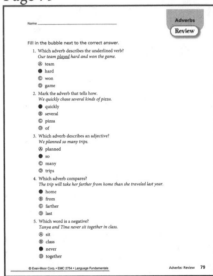

Fill in the bubble next to the correct answer.

1. Which adverb describes the underlined verb?
   Our team played hard and won the game.
   Ⓐ team
   ● hard
   Ⓒ won
   Ⓓ game

2. Mark the adverb that tells how.
   We quickly chose several kinds of pizza.
   ● quickly
   Ⓑ several
   Ⓒ pizza
   Ⓓ of

3. Which adverb describes an adjective?
   We planned so many trips.
   Ⓐ planned
   ● so
   Ⓒ many
   Ⓓ trips

4. Which adverb compares?
   The trip will take her farther from home than she traveled last year.
   Ⓐ home
   Ⓑ from
   ● farther
   Ⓓ last

5. Which word is a negative?
   Tanya and Tina never sit together in class.
   Ⓐ sit
   Ⓑ class
   ● never
   Ⓓ together

© Evan-Moor Corp. • EMC 2754 • Language Fundamentals Adverbs: Review 79

Page 80

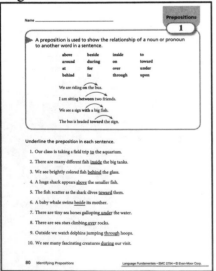

A preposition is used to show the relationship of a noun or pronoun to another word in a sentence.

above	beside	inside	to
around	during	on	toward
at	for	over	under
behind	in	through	upon

We are riding on the bus.
I am sitting between two friends.
We see a sign with a big fish.
The bus is headed toward the sign.

Underline the preposition in each sentence.

1. Our class is taking a field trip to the aquarium.
2. There are many different fish inside the big tanks.
3. We see brightly colored fish behind the glass.
4. A huge shark appears above the smaller fish.
5. The fish scatter as the shark dives toward them.
6. A baby whale swims beside its mother.
7. There are tiny sea horses galloping under the water.
8. There are sea stars climbing over rocks.
9. Outside we watch dolphins jumping through hoops.
10. We see many fascinating creatures during our visit.

80 Identifying Prepositions Language Fundamentals • EMC 2754 • © Evan-Moor Corp.

Page 81

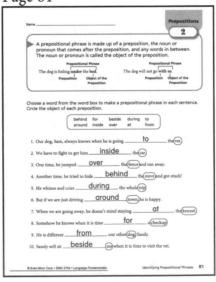

A prepositional phrase is made up of a preposition, the noun or pronoun that comes after the preposition, and any words in between. The noun or pronoun is called the object of the preposition.

Prepositional Phrase
The dog is hiding under the bed.
Preposition Object of the Preposition

The dog will not go with us.
Preposition Object of the Preposition

Choose a word from the word box to make a prepositional phrase in each sentence. Circle the object of each preposition.

behind for beside during to
around inside over at from

1. Our dog, Sam, always knows when he is going __to__ the (vet).
2. We have to fight to get him __inside__ the (car).
3. One time, he jumped __over__ the (fence) and ran away.
4. Another time, he tried to hide __behind__ the (stove) and got stuck!
5. He whines and cries __during__ the whole (trip).
6. But if we are just driving __around__ (town) he is happy.
7. When we are going away, he doesn't mind staying __at__ the (kennel).
8. Somehow he knows when it is time __for__ a (checkup).
9. He is different __from__ our other (dog) Sandy.
10. Sandy will sit __beside__ (me) when it is time to visit the vet.

© Evan-Moor Corp. • EMC 2754 • Language Fundamentals Identifying Prepositional Phrases 81

Page 82

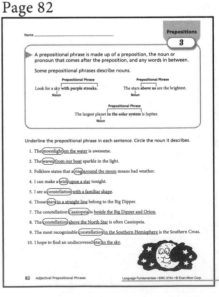

A prepositional phrase is made up of a preposition, the noun or pronoun that comes after the preposition, and any words in between. Some prepositional phrases describe nouns.

Prepositional Phrase
Look for a sky with purple streaks.
Noun

Prepositional Phrase
The stars above us are the brightest.
Noun

Prepositional Phrase
The largest planet in the solar system is Jupiter.
Noun

Underline the prepositional phrase in each sentence. Circle the noun it describes.

1. The (moonlight) on the water is awesome.
2. The (waves) from our boat sparkle in the light.
3. Folklore states that a (ring) around the moon means bad weather.
4. I can make a (wish) upon a star tonight.
5. I see a (constellation) with a familiar shape.
6. Those (stars) in a straight line belong to the Big Dipper.
7. The constellation (Cassiopeia) is beside the Big Dipper and Orion.
8. The (constellation) above the North Star is often Cassiopeia.
9. The most recognizable (constellation) in the Southern Hemisphere is the Southern Cross.
10. I hope to find an undiscovered (star) in the sky.

82 Adjectival Prepositional Phrases Language Fundamentals • EMC 2754 • © Evan-Moor Corp.

Page 83

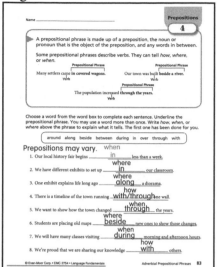

Prepositions 4

A prepositional phrase is made up of a preposition, the noun or pronoun that is the object of the preposition, and any words in between.

Some prepositional phrases describe verbs. They can tell *how*, *where*, or *when*.

Many settlers came **in covered wagons.**
Our town was built **beside a river.**
The population increased **through the years.**

Choose a word from the word box to complete each sentence. Underline the prepositional phrase. You may use a word more than once. Write *how*, *when*, or *where* above the phrase to explain what it tells. The first one has been done for you.

around along beside between during in over through with

Prepositions may vary.

1. Our local history fair begins *in* less than a week. (when)
2. We have different exhibits to set up *in* our classroom. (where)
3. One exhibit explains life long ago *along* a diorama. (where)
4. There is a timeline of the town running *with/through* the wall. (how)
5. We want to show how the town changed *through* the years. (when)
6. Students are placing old maps *beside* new ones to show those changes. (where)
7. We will have many classes visiting *during* morning and afternoon hours. (when)
8. We're proud that we are sharing our knowledge *with* others. (how)

Page 84

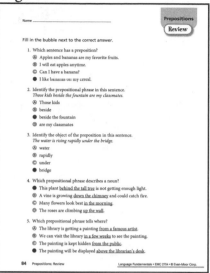

Prepositions Review

Fill in the bubble next to the correct answer.

1. Which sentence has a preposition?
   - Ⓐ Apples and bananas are my favorite fruits.
   - Ⓑ I will eat apples anytime.
   - Ⓒ Can I have a banana?
   - ● I like bananas on my cereal.

2. Identify the prepositional phrase in this sentence. *Those kids beside the fountain are my classmates.*
   - Ⓐ Those kids
   - Ⓑ beside
   - ● beside the fountain
   - Ⓓ are my classmates

3. Identify the object of the preposition in this sentence. *The water is rising rapidly under the bridge.*
   - Ⓐ water
   - Ⓑ rapidly
   - Ⓒ under
   - ● bridge

4. Which prepositional phrase describes a noun?
   - ● This plant behind the tall tree is not getting enough light.
   - Ⓑ A vine is growing down the chimney and could catch fire.
   - Ⓒ Many flowers look best in the morning.
   - Ⓓ The roses are climbing up the wall.

5. Which prepositional phrase tells where?
   - Ⓐ The library is getting a painting from a famous artist.
   - Ⓑ We can visit the library in a few weeks to see the painting.
   - Ⓒ The painting is kept hidden from the public.
   - ● The painting will be displayed above the librarian's desk.

Page 85

Sentences 1

A sentence is a group of words that express a complete thought. A statement is a sentence that tells something. It ends with a period (.).

Winter is cold and flu season.
I have a cold.

Answer each question with a statement. Make sure that each statement is a complete sentence that begins with a capital letter and ends with a period.

1. When do people usually go on vacation?
   Answers will vary, but must follow directions.

2. In what season do the leaves fall from the trees?

3. In what season do the first buds blossom?

4. Where would you like to go on vacation?

Write a statement on each topic below. Make sure that each statement is a complete sentence that begins with a capital letter and ends with a period.

5. (Saturdays) **Answers will vary.**

6. (dessert)

Page 86

Sentences 2

A question is a sentence that asks something. It ends with a question mark (?).

Are you having fun at the amusement park?
Have you seen the roller coaster?

Many questions begin with one of these words:
who what where when why how

Answers will vary, suggested answers given.

Write a question that might be followed by the given answer. Be sure to begin the question with a capital letter and end it with a question mark.

1. Question: **Why is that ride called a Ferris wheel?**
   Answer: It is called a Ferris wheel because it was invented by Mr. G. W. G. Ferris.

2. Question: **When was the Ferris wheel invented?**
   Answer: Mr. Ferris invented his famous ride in the year 1893.

3. Question: **What is your favorite ride?**
   Answer: My favorite ride is the tilt-a-whirl.

4. Question: **How many times did you ride it?**
   Answer: I rode it four times yesterday.

Write a question about each subject.

5. (inventions) **Answers will vary.**
6. (roller coasters)
7. (picnics)
8. (cotton candy)

Page 87

Sentences 3

An exclamation is a sentence that expresses a strong feeling. It ends with an exclamation point (!).

The circus is coming to town! Here comes the parade!

Sometimes an exclamation is just one or two words long.

Wow! Look! Oh, no!

One of the sentences in each pair is an exclamation and the other is a statement. Add the correct punctuation mark to the end of each sentence.

1. Uncle Fred is taking us to the circus. What fun it will be!
2. I can't wait! We're going on Saturday.
3. I have our tickets ready. We are finally here!
4. Oh, listen! The band is starting to play.

Describe each picture with an exclamation.

5. **Answers will vary.**
6.

Page 88

Sentences 4

An imperative sentence gives a command. It ends with a period (.).

Close the door.
Open the windows.

Some imperative sentences contain a courtesy word such as *please*.

Please come quickly.
Clean your room, **please.**

Underline the imperative sentences.

1. This room is a mess! Pick up your socks.
2. Is that a candy wrapper under your bed? Throw it away.
3. Hang up the clean clothes. I will wash these.
4. Next, we'll organize this closet. Open the door, please.

Study the picture of the messy room. Write two imperative sentences an adult could be saying to the child.

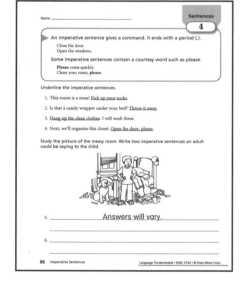

5. **Answers will vary.**
6.

Page 89

Sentences 5

A sentence is a group of words that express a complete thought. There are four kinds of sentences.

- A statement tells something. It ends with a period (.).
  Enrico Caruso was a famous singer.
- A question asks something. It ends with a question mark (?).
  Have you heard of him?
- An exclamation shows strong feeling. It ends with an exclamation point (!).
  He had a fantastic voice!
- An imperative sentence gives a command. It ends with a period (.).
  Play this recording.

What kind of sentence is it? Write *statement, question, imperative,* or *exclamation* on the line. Then add the correct punctuation mark to the sentence.

1. Hand me that CD. — **imperative**
2. Caruso was an opera singer. — **statement**
3. Do you like opera? — **question**
4. I love it! — **exclamation**
5. My sister hates it! — **exclamation**
6. Listen closely to Caruso's voice. — **imperative**
7. An opera tells a story with music. — **statement**
8. Would you like to listen to my favorite opera? — **question**
9. My favorite opera is *The Magic Flute.* — **statement**
10. How beautiful it is! — **exclamation**

Page 90

Sentences 6

A group of words that is punctuated like a sentence, but does not have both a subject and a predicate, is called a sentence fragment. A fragment is not a complete sentence. It does not express a complete thought.

Sentence Fragment   Ate dinner in a restaurant last night.
Sentence Fragment   My parents.
Complete Sentence   My parents ate dinner in a restaurant last night.

Label each group of words below as either a complete sentence or a fragment.

1. Last Saturday night at my house. — fragment
2. Our big brother was in charge. — complete sentence
3. We watched a movie. — complete sentence
4. About two kids and their parents on Mars. — fragment
5. The story was science fiction. — complete sentence
6. Pizza and a big salad with lots of crunchy vegetables. — fragment
7. We ate pizza and salad. — complete sentence
8. Had pepperoni and mushrooms. — fragment
9. Climbed into bed very late! — fragment
10. Our parents came home even later! — complete sentence

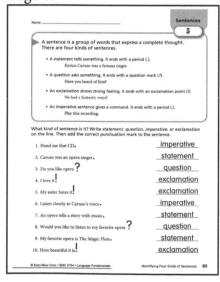

Page 91

Sentences 7

A sentence fragment is **not** a complete sentence. It does **not** express a complete thought.

Sentence Fragment
A tasty stew of beef, carrots, potatoes, and onions.
Juan and Ella in the kitchen.
Prepared the table for dinner.

To turn a fragment into a complete sentence, add missing information. Make sure that the sentence has both a subject and a predicate.

Subject	Predicate
A tasty stew	simmers on the stove.
Juan and Ella	stirred the pot in the kitchen.
They	set the table for dinner.

Turn each sentence fragment below into a complete sentence by adding missing information. Write the sentence on the line.

1. My mother and father in the dining room.
   Answers will vary.
2. Opened the door for our guests.
3. Mr. Hirata and his daughter.
4. Heard the doorbell ring again.
5. Everyone at the table.

Page 92

Name _____

Fill in the bubble next to the correct answer.

1. Which group of words is a fragment?
   Ⓐ What was that sound?
   Ⓑ I'm scared!
   Ⓒ Tell a funny story, please.
   ● Late at night in the backyard.

2. Which example turns this fragment into a complete sentence?
   With the flashlight.
   Ⓐ With the flashlight, Grace and I.
   Ⓑ Grace and I with the flashlight.
   ● I explored the backyard with the flashlight.
   Ⓓ In the backyard with the flashlight.

3. Read the sentence. Choose the correct sentence type.
   Don't scratch that mosquito bite.
   Ⓐ statement
   Ⓑ question
   Ⓒ exclamation
   ● imperative

4. Read the sentence. Choose the correct sentence type.
   That owl scared me!
   Ⓐ statement
   Ⓑ question
   ● exclamation
   Ⓓ imperative

5. Which sentence ends with the correct punctuation mark?
   Ⓐ The lotion smells a little funny?
   ● Has the itching stopped?
   Ⓒ Mosquitoes are common in the summer!
   Ⓓ Stop scratching, please?

92   Sentences: Review 1   Language Fundamentals • EMC 2754 • © Evan-Moor Corp.

Page 93

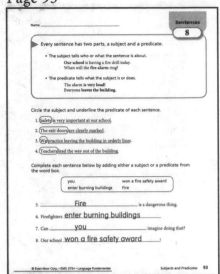

Name _____

▶ Every sentence has two parts, a subject and a predicate.
   • The subject tells who or what the sentence is about.
     Our school is having a fire drill today.
     When will the **fire alarm** ring?
   • The predicate tells what the subject is or does.
     The alarm **is very loud!**
     Everyone **leaves the building.**

Circle the subject and underline the predicate of each sentence.

1. (Safety) is very important at our school.
2. The (exit doors) are clearly marked.
3. (We) practice leaving the building in orderly lines.
4. (Teachers) lead the way out of the building.

Complete each sentence below by adding either a subject or a predicate from the word box.

| you | won a fire safety award |
| enter burning buildings | Fire |

5. _____ Fire _____ is a dangerous thing.

6. Firefighters _enter burning buildings_

7. Can _____ you _____ imagine doing that?

8. Our school _won a fire safety award_

© Evan-Moor Corp. • EMC 2754 • Language Fundamentals   Subjects and Predicates   93

Page 94

Name _____

▶ A complete sentence has two parts, a subject and a predicate.
   • The subject names the person, place, or thing that the sentence is about.
   • The predicate tells what the subject is or does.

Subject	Predicate
The storm	came without warning.
The funnel of wind	swirled violently.

Draw one line under the subject and two lines under the predicate in each sentence.

1. The whole family listens to the radio each morning.
2. The radio sits on the kitchen counter.
3. Jeremy waits for the weather report.
4. The forecast calls for rain in the afternoon.
5. An umbrella will be necessary.

Read each sentence. Then write each sentence part on the lines below.

6. The dark clouds gathered over the playground.
   Subject: _The dark clouds_ Predicate: _gathered over the playground._

7. All of the children watched the clouds.
   Subject: _All of the children_ Predicate: _watched the clouds._

8. The rain is falling hard now.
   Subject: _The rain_ Predicate: _is falling hard now._

94   Subjects and Predicates   Language Fundamentals • EMC 2754 • © Evan-Moor Corp.

Page 95

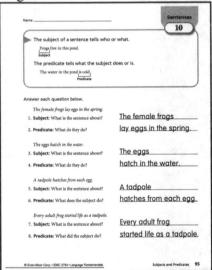

Name _____

▶ The subject of a sentence tells who or what.
   Frogs live in this pond.
   —— Subject ——
   The predicate tells what the subject does or is.
   The water in the pond is cold.
   —— Predicate ——

Answer each question below.

The female frogs lay eggs in the spring.

1. Subject: What is the sentence about?   _The female frogs_
2. Predicate: What do they do?   _lay eggs in the spring._

The eggs hatch in the water.

3. Subject: What is the sentence about?   _The eggs_
4. Predicate: What do they do?   _hatch in the water._

A tadpole hatches from each egg.

5. Subject: What is the sentence about?   _A tadpole_
6. Predicate: What does the subject do?   _hatches from each egg._

Every adult frog started life as a tadpole.

7. Subject: What is the sentence about?   _Every adult frog_
8. Predicate: What did the subject do?   _started life as a tadpole._

© Evan-Moor Corp. • EMC 2754 • Language Fundamentals   Subjects and Predicates   95

Page 96

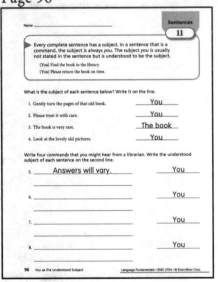

Name _____

▶ Every complete sentence has a subject. In a sentence that is a command, the subject is always you. The subject you is usually not stated in the sentence but is understood to be the subject.
   (You) Find the book in the library.
   (You) Please return the book on time.

What is the subject of each sentence below? Write it on the line.

1. Gently turn the pages of that old book.   _You_
2. Please treat it with care.   _You_
3. The book is very rare.   _The book_
4. Look at the lovely old pictures.   _You_

Write four commands that you might hear from a librarian. Write the understood subject of each sentence on the second line.

5. _Answers will vary._   _You_

6. _____   _You_

7. _____   _You_

8. _____   _You_

96   You as the Understood Subject   Language Fundamentals • EMC 2754 • © Evan-Moor Corp.

Page 97

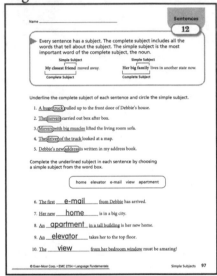

Name _____

▶ Every sentence has a subject. The complete subject includes all the words that tell about the subject. The simple subject is the most important word of the complete subject, the noun.

Simple Subject	Simple Subject
My closest **friend** moved away.	Her big **family** lives in another state now.
Complete Subject	Complete Subject

Underline the complete subject of each sentence and circle the simple subject.

1. A huge (truck) pulled up to the front door of Debbie's house.
2. The (movers) carried out box after box.
3. (Movers) with big muscles lifted the living room sofa.
4. The (driver) of the truck looked at a map.
5. Debbie's new (address) is written in my address book.

Complete the underlined subject in each sentence by choosing a simple subject from the word box.

| home   elevator   e-mail   view   apartment |

6. The first _e-mail_ from Debbie has arrived.
7. Her new _home_ is in a big city.
8. An _apartment_ in a tall building is her new home.
9. An _elevator_ takes her to the top floor.
10. The _view_ from her bedroom window must be amazing!

© Evan-Moor Corp. • EMC 2754 • Language Fundamentals   Simple Subjects   97

Page 98

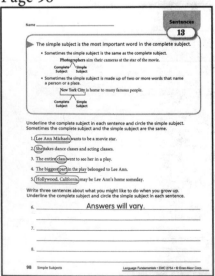

Name _____

▶ The simple subject is the most important word in the complete subject.
   • Sometimes the simple subject is the same as the complete subject.
     Photographers aim their cameras at the star of the movie.
     Complete / Simple
     Subject / Subject
   • Sometimes the simple subject is made up of two or more words that name a person or a place.
     New York City is home to many famous people.
     Complete / Simple
     Subject / Subject

Underline the complete subject in each sentence and circle the simple subject. Sometimes the complete subject and the simple subject are the same.

1. (Lee Ann Michaels) wants to be a movie star.
2. (She) takes dance classes and acting classes.
3. The entire (class) went to see her in a play.
4. The biggest (part) in the play belonged to Lee Ann.
5. (Hollywood, California) may be Lee Ann's home someday.

Write three sentences about what you might like to do when you grow up. Underline the complete subject and circle the simple subject in each sentence.

6. _Answers will vary._

7. _____

8. _____

98   Simple Subjects   Language Fundamentals • EMC 2754 • © Evan-Moor Corp.

Page 99

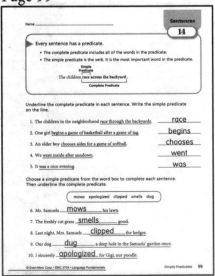

Name _____

▶ Every sentence has a predicate.
   • The complete predicate includes all of the words in the predicate.
   • The simple predicate is the verb. It is the most important word in the predicate.
     Simple
     Predicate
     The children **race** across the backyard.
     —— Complete Predicate ——

Underline the complete predicate in each sentence. Write the simple predicate on the line.

1. The children in the neighborhood race through the backyards.   _race_
2. One girl begins a game of basketball after a game of tag.   _begins_
3. An older boy chooses sides for a game of softball.   _chooses_
4. We went inside after sundown.   _went_
5. It was a nice evening.   _was_

Choose a simple predicate from the word box to complete each sentence. Then underline the complete predicate.

| mows   apologized   clipped   smells   dug |

6. Mr. Samuels _mows_ his lawn.
7. The freshly cut grass _smells_ good.
8. Last night, Mrs. Samuels _clipped_ the hedges.
9. Our dog _dug_ a deep hole in the Samuels' garden once.
10. I sincerely _apologized_ for Gigi, our poodle.

© Evan-Moor Corp. • EMC 2754 • Language Fundamentals   Simple Predicates   99

Page 100

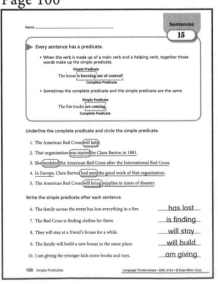

Name _____

▶ Every sentence has a predicate.
   • When the verb is made up of a main verb and a helping verb, together those words make up the simple predicate.
     Simple Predicate
     The house **is burning** out of control!
     —— Complete Predicate ——
   • Sometimes the complete predicate and the simple predicate are the same.
     Simple Predicate
     The fire trucks **are coming.**
     —— Complete Predicate ——

Underline the complete predicate and circle the simple predicate.

1. The American Red Cross (will help).
2. That organization (was started) by Clara Barton in 1881.
3. She (modeled) the American Red Cross after the International Red Cross.
4. In Europe, Clara Barton (had seen) the good work of that organization.
5. The American Red Cross (will bring) supplies in times of disaster.

Write the simple predicate after each sentence.

6. The family across the street has lost everything in a fire.   _has lost_
7. The Red Cross is finding clothes for them.   _is finding_
8. They will stay at a friend's house for a while.   _will stay_
9. The family will build a new house in the same place.   _will build_
10. I am giving the younger kids some books and toys.   _am giving_

100   Simple Predicates   Language Fundamentals • EMC 2754 • © Evan-Moor Corp.

Page 101

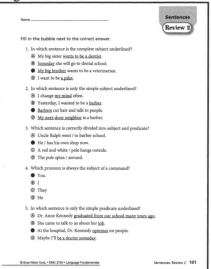

Name ______________________

Sentences
Review 2

Fill in the bubble next to the correct answer.

1. In which sentence is the complete subject underlined?
   - Ⓐ My big sister wants to be a dentist.
   - Ⓑ Someday she will go to dental school.
   - ● My big brother wants to be a veterinarian.
   - Ⓓ I want to be a pilot.
2. In which sentence is only the simple subject underlined?
   - Ⓐ I change my mind often.
   - Ⓑ Yesterday, I wanted to be a barber.
   - ● Barbers cut hair and talk to people.
   - Ⓓ My next-door neighbor is a barber.
3. Which sentence is correctly divided into subject and predicate?
   - Ⓐ Uncle Ralph went / to barber school.
   - ● He / has his own shop now.
   - Ⓒ A red and white / pole hangs outside.
   - Ⓓ The pole spins / around.
4. Which pronoun is always the subject of a command?
   - ● You
   - Ⓑ I
   - Ⓒ They
   - Ⓓ He
5. In which sentence is only the simple predicate underlined?
   - Ⓐ Dr. Anne Kennedy graduated from our school many years ago.
   - Ⓑ She came to talk to us about her job.
   - ● At the hospital, Dr. Kennedy operates on people.
   - Ⓓ Maybe I'll be a doctor someday.

© Evan-Moor Corp. • EMC 2754 • Language Fundamentals — Sentences: Review 2 101

Page 102

Name ______________________

Sentences
16

A simple sentence contains a subject and a predicate. A simple sentence can be short or long.

Subject: Carla — Predicate: cooks.
Subject: She — Predicate: stirs a pot full of potatoes and ham.

Write each sentence part on the lines below.

1. Italian food is my favorite kind of food.
   Italian food (complete subject) — is my favorite kind of food. (complete predicate)
2. My grandmother makes Polish food.
   My grandmother (complete subject) — makes Polish food. (complete predicate)
3. I like stuffed cabbage.
   I (complete subject) — like stuffed cabbage. (complete predicate)
4. Peanut butter sandwiches are good, too.
   Peanut butter sandwiches (complete subject) — are good, too. (complete predicate)

Write your own simple sentences about your favorite foods. Then circle the complete subject and underline the complete predicate.

5. Answers will vary.
6. ______________________
7. ______________________
8. ______________________

102 Simple Sentences — Language Fundamentals • EMC 2754 • © Evan-Moor Corp.

Page 103

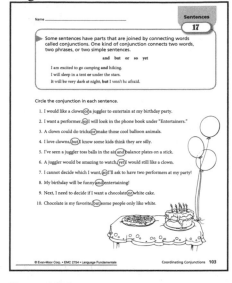

Name ______________________

Sentences
17

Some sentences have parts that are joined by connecting words called conjunctions. One kind of conjunction connects two words, two phrases, or two simple sentences.

and but or so yet

I am excited to go camping **and** hiking.
I will sleep in a tent **or** under the stars.
It will be very dark at night, **but** I won't be afraid.

Circle the conjunction in each sentence.

1. I would like a clown (or) a juggler to entertain at my birthday party.
2. I want a performer, (so) I will look in the phone book under "Entertainers."
3. A clown could do tricks (or) make those cool balloon animals.
4. I love clowns, (but) I know some kids think they are silly.
5. I've seen a juggler toss balls in the air (and) balance plates on a stick.
6. A juggler would be amazing to watch, (yet) I would still like a clown.
7. I cannot decide which I want, (so) I'll ask to have two performers at my party!
8. My birthday will be funny (and) entertaining!
9. Next, I need to decide if I want a chocolate (or) white cake.
10. Chocolate is my favorite, (but) some people only like white.

© Evan-Moor Corp. • EMC 2754 • Language Fundamentals — Coordinating Conjunctions 103

Page 104

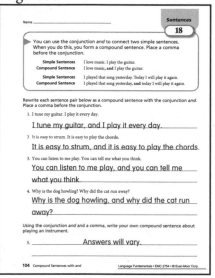

Name ______________________

Sentences
18

You can use the conjunction *and* to connect two simple sentences. When you do this, you form a compound sentence. Place a comma before the conjunction.

Simple Sentences	I love music. I play the guitar.
Compound Sentence	I love music, **and** I play the guitar.
Simple Sentences	I played that song yesterday. Today I will play it again.
Compound Sentence	I played that song yesterday, **and** today I will play it again.

Rewrite each sentence pair below as a compound sentence with the conjunction *and*. Place a comma before the conjunction.

1. I tune my guitar. I play it every day.
   I tune my guitar, and I play it every day.
2. It is easy to strum. It is easy to play the chords.
   It is easy to strum, and it is easy to play the chords.
3. You can listen to me play. You can tell me what you think.
   You can listen to me play, and you can tell me what you think.
4. Why is the dog howling? Why did the cat run away?
   Why is the dog howling, and why did the cat run away?

Using the conjunction *and* and a comma, write your own compound sentence about playing an instrument.

5. Answers will vary.

104 Compound Sentences with *and* — Language Fundamentals • EMC 2754 • © Evan-Moor Corp.

Page 105

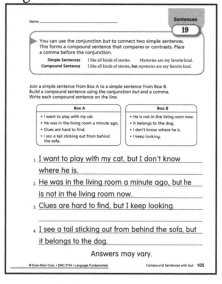

Name ______________________

Sentences
19

You can use the conjunction *but* to connect two simple sentences. This forms a compound sentence that compares or contrasts. Place a comma before the conjunction.

Simple Sentences	I like all kinds of stories. Mysteries are my favorite kind.
Compound Sentence	I like all kinds of stories, **but** mysteries are my favorite kind.

Join a simple sentence from Box A to a simple sentence from Box B. Build a compound sentence using the conjunction *but* and a comma. Write each compound sentence on the line.

Box A	Box B
• I want to play with my cat. • He was in the living room a minute ago. • Clues are hard to find. • I see a tail sticking out from behind the sofa.	• He is not in the living room now. • It belongs to the dog. • I don't know where he is. • I keep looking.

1. I want to play with my cat, but I don't know where he is.
2. He was in the living room a minute ago, but he is not in the living room now.
3. Clues are hard to find, but I keep looking.
4. I see a tail sticking out from behind the sofa, but it belongs to the dog.

Answers may vary.

© Evan-Moor Corp. • EMC 2754 • Language Fundamentals — Compound Sentences with *but* 105

Page 106

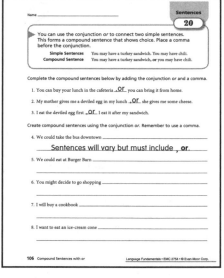

Name ______________________

Sentences
20

You can use the conjunction *or* to connect two simple sentences. This forms a compound sentence that shows choice. Place a comma before the conjunction.

Simple Sentences	You may have a turkey sandwich. You may have chili.
Compound Sentence	You may have a turkey sandwich, **or** you may have chili.

Complete the compound sentences below by adding the conjunction *or* and a comma.

1. You can buy your lunch in the cafeteria , or you can bring it from home.
2. My mother gives me a deviled egg in my lunch , or she gives me some cheese.
3. I eat the deviled egg first , or I eat it after my sandwich.

Create compound sentences using the conjunction *or*. Remember to use a comma.

4. We could take the bus downtown ______
   Sentences will vary but must include **, or.**
5. We could eat at Burger Barn ______
6. You might decide to go shopping ______
7. I will buy a cookbook ______
8. I want to eat an ice-cream cone ______

106 Compound Sentences with *or* — Language Fundamentals • EMC 2754 • © Evan-Moor Corp.

Page 107

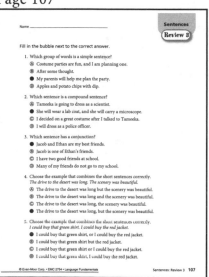

Name ______________________

Sentences
Review 3

Fill in the bubble next to the correct answer.

1. Which group of words is a simple sentence?
   - Ⓐ Costume parties are fun, and I am planning one.
   - Ⓑ After some thought.
   - ● My parents will help me plan the party.
   - Ⓓ Apples and potato chips with dip.
2. Which sentence is a compound sentence?
   - Ⓐ Tameeka is going to dress as a scientist.
   - ● She will wear a lab coat, and she will carry a microscope.
   - Ⓒ I decided on a great costume after I talked to Tameeka.
   - Ⓓ I will dress as a police officer.
3. Which sentence has a conjunction?
   - ● Jacob and Ethan are my best friends.
   - Ⓑ Jacob is one of Ethan's friends.
   - Ⓒ I have two good friends at school.
   - Ⓓ Many of my friends do not go to my school.
4. Choose the example that combines the short sentences correctly.
   The drive to the desert was long. The scenery was beautiful.
   - Ⓐ The drive to the desert was long but the scenery was beautiful.
   - Ⓑ The drive to the desert was long and the scenery was beautiful.
   - Ⓒ The drive to the desert was long, the scenery was beautiful.
   - ● The drive to the desert was long, but the scenery was beautiful.
5. Choose the example that combines the short sentences correctly.
   I could buy that green shirt. I could buy the red jacket.
   - ● I could buy that green shirt, or I could buy the red jacket.
   - Ⓑ I could buy that green shirt but the red jacket.
   - Ⓒ I could buy that green shirt or I could buy the red jacket.
   - Ⓓ I could buy that green shirt, I could buy the red jacket.

© Evan-Moor Corp. • EMC 2754 • Language Fundamentals — Sentences: Review 3 107

Page 108

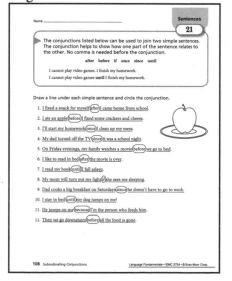

Name ______________________

Sentences
21

The conjunctions listed below can be used to join two simple sentences. The conjunction helps to show how one part of the sentence relates to the other. No comma is needed before the conjunction.

after before if once since until

I cannot play video games. I finish my homework.
I cannot play video games **until** I finish my homework.

Draw a line under each simple sentence and circle the conjunction.

1. I fixed a snack for myself (after) I came home from school.
2. I ate an apple (before) I fixed some crackers and cheese.
3. I'll start my homework (once) I clean up my mess.
4. My dad turned off the TV (since) it was a school night.
5. On Friday evenings, my family watches a movie (before) we go to bed.
6. I like to read in bed (after) the movie is over.
7. I read my book (until) I fall asleep.
8. My mom will turn out my light (if) she sees me sleeping.
9. Dad cooks a big breakfast on Saturdays (since) he doesn't have to go to work.
10. I stay in bed (until) my dog jumps on me!
11. He jumps on me (because) I'm the person who feeds him.
12. Then we go downstairs (before) all the food is gone.

108 Subordinating Conjunctions — Language Fundamentals • EMC 2754 • © Evan-Moor Corp.

Page 109

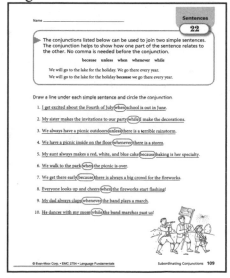

Name ______________________

Sentences
22

The conjunctions listed below can be used to join two simple sentences. The conjunction helps to show how one part of the sentence relates to the other. No comma is needed before the conjunction.

because unless when whenever while

We will go to the lake for the holiday. We go there every year.
We will go to the lake for the holiday **because** we go there every year.

Draw a line under each simple sentence and circle the conjunction.

1. I get excited about the Fourth of July (when) school is out in June.
2. My sister makes the invitations to our party (while) I make the decorations.
3. We always have a picnic outdoors (unless) there is a terrible rainstorm.
4. We have a picnic inside on the floor (whenever) there is a storm.
5. My aunt always makes a red, white, and blue cake (because) baking is her specialty.
6. We walk to the park (when) the picnic is over.
7. We get there early (because) there is always a big crowd for the fireworks.
8. Everyone looks up and cheers (when) the fireworks start flashing!
9. My dad always claps (whenever) the band plays a march.
10. He dances with my mom (while) the band marches past us!

© Evan-Moor Corp. • EMC 2754 • Language Fundamentals — Subordinating Conjunctions 109

Page 110

Name ____________________

Sentences 23

The conjunctions listed below can be used to join two simple sentences. The conjunction helps to show how one part of the sentence relates to the other. No comma is needed before the conjunction.

after	because	before
if	once	since
unless	until	when
whenever	while	where

I am reading about Egypt. I am interested in pyramids.
I am reading about Egypt **because** I am interested in pyramids.

Tourists climb the pyramids. They ride camels into the desert.
Tourists climb the pyramids **after** they ride camels into the desert.

Choose the conjunction from the rule box to correctly combine the parts of each sentence.

1. The pyramids are amazing because they are so huge and so old.
2. The builders did not have big cranes when the pyramids were built.
3. I have looked at many photographs since I started reading about Egypt.
4. I decided to study Egypt after I saw a photograph of the Sphinx.
5. I am going to make a model of the Sphinx before I present my report to the class.
6. I learned about a famous dam in Egypt while I was doing my research.
7. Egypt's electricity supply doubled once the High Dam was built at Aswan.
8. I will be an expert on Egypt if/once I read all these books!

110 Subordinating Conjunctions — Language Fundamentals • EMC 2754 • © Evan-Moor Corp.

Page 111

Name ____________________

Sentences 24

Combine short sentences by moving key words or phrases from one sentence to another.

Short Sentences Alex read a book. It was about a mysterious house.
Combined Alex read a book about a mysterious house.
Short Sentences The old house had an attic. The attic had dark windows.
Combined The old house had an attic with dark windows.

Combine each sentence pair by moving words and phrases from one sentence to the other. Sometimes you may need to add words.

1. The mysterious house was old. It had squeaky doors.
   The mysterious old house had squeaky doors.
2. The house was hidden. It was hidden by thick trees.
   The house was hidden by thick trees.
3. Slowly, the children approached the house. They took their dog.
   Slowly, the children approached the house with their dog.
4. Their dog barked. He barked at the cat in the window.
   Their dog barked at the cat in the window.
5. Ms. Kinley lived in the house. She lived with her cat.
   Ms. Kinley lived in the house with her cat.
6. Ms. Kinley needed help. She needed help cleaning out her mysterious attic.
   Ms. Kinley needed help cleaning out her mysterious attic.

Answers may vary.

© Evan-Moor Corp. • EMC 2754 • Language Fundamentals — Sentence Combining 111

Page 112

Name ____________________

Sentences Review 4

Fill in the bubble next to the correct answer. Choose the example that combines the short sentences correctly.

1. *The class painted a mural. We painted it for the school office.*
   - ● The class painted a mural for the school office.
   - Ⓑ The class painted a mural, we painted it for the school office.
   - Ⓒ The class painted a mural and put it in the school office.
   - Ⓓ The class painted a mural in the school office.
2. *The leaves change colors in the fall. The pine needles stay green.*
   - Ⓐ The leaves change colors in the fall, the pine needles stay green.
   - Ⓑ The leaves change colors in the fall or the pine needles stay green.
   - ● The leaves change colors in the fall while the pine needles stay green.
   - Ⓓ The leaves change colors in the fall the pine needles stay green.
3. *Jenny's shirt has buttons. The buttons are round.*
   - ● Jenny's shirt has round buttons.
   - Ⓑ Jenny's shirt has buttons and they are round.
   - Ⓒ Jenny's shirt has buttons, while the buttons are round.
   - Ⓓ Jenny's shirt has buttons while they are round.
4. *Her dog snores. It has a short nose.*
   - Ⓐ Her dog snores, or it has a short nose.
   - Ⓑ Her dog snores, it has a short nose.
   - Ⓒ Her dog's short nose snores.
   - ● Her dog snores because it has a short nose.
5. *Ryan went to a movie. He ate popcorn.*
   - Ⓐ Ryan went to a movie while he ate popcorn.
   - Ⓑ Ryan went to a movie, but he ate popcorn.
   - ● Ryan went to a movie where he ate popcorn.
   - Ⓓ Ryan went to a movie and popcorn.

112 Sentences: Review 4 — Language Fundamentals • EMC 2754 • © Evan-Moor Corp.

Page 113

Name ____________________

Sentences 25

A run-on sentence is made up of two or more sentences that run together without punctuation or a connecting word. You can correct a run-on sentence by forming two sentences.

Run-on Sentence The ice on the pond is solid Kenny wants to go ice-skating.
Correction The ice on the pond is solid. Kenny wants to go ice-skating.
Run-on Sentence He carries his skates an extra scarf is a good idea, too.
Correction He carries his skates. An extra scarf is a good idea, too.

Correct each run-on sentence by dividing it into two simple sentences. Write the new sentences on the line.

1. The ice on the pond is thick we can skate safely.
   The ice on the pond is thick. We can skate safely.
2. There is Mr. Graff he is doing a fancy turn.
   There is Mr. Graff. He is doing a fancy turn.
3. Sherry and Tyler hold hands they skate around and around.
   Sherry and Tyler hold hands. They skate around and around.
4. The littlest kids wobble that one keeps falling down.
   The littlest kids wobble. That one keeps falling down.
5. Some moms and dads have built a fire we can get warm.
   Some moms and dads have built a fire. We can get warm.

© Evan-Moor Corp. • EMC 2754 • Language Fundamentals — Run-on Sentences 113

Page 114

Name ____________________

Sentences 26

You can correct a run-on sentence by forming two sentences.

Run-on Sentence Mother's Day is coming I have five dollars to spend.
Correction Mother's Day is coming. I have five dollars to spend.
Run-on Sentence My mom likes flowers roses are her favorite.
Correction My mom likes flowers. Roses are her favorite.

Correct each run-on sentence by dividing it into two simple sentences. Write the new sentences on the line.

1. I made a special gift for Mother's Day I worked a long time on it.
   I made a special gift for Mother's Day. I worked a long time on it.
2. I want to show my mom how much I appreciate her I made a giant card.
   I want to show my mom how much I appreciate her. I made a giant card.
3. The card is as tall as my dad he will help me hold it.
   The card is as tall as my dad. He will help me hold it.
4. I hope she loves the card I want this to be her best Mother's Day yet.
   I hope she loves the card. I want this to be the best Mother's Day yet!

114 Run-on Sentences — Language Fundamentals • EMC 2754 • © Evan-Moor Corp.

Page 115

Name ____________________

Sentences 27

You can correct a run-on sentence by adding a comma and a conjunction such as *and, but,* or *or* to make a compound sentence.

Run-on David designed the costumes Mark designed the stage sets.
Correction David designed the costumes, **and** Mark designed the stage sets.
Run-on Leslie will audition for the play she doesn't want the lead.
Correction Leslie will audition for the play, **but** she doesn't want the lead.

Rewrite each run-on sentence correctly by adding a comma and a conjunction.

1. Leslie likes to sing she can't dance.
   Leslie likes to sing, but she can't dance.
2. Jackson wants the lead in the play he has a good chance of getting it.
   Jackson wants the lead in the play, and he has a good chance of getting it.
3. Jackson can sing he can dance, too.
   Jackson can sing, and he can dance, too.
4. Everyone wants to hear Jackson sing he has a sore throat.
   Everyone wants to hear Jackson sing, but he has a sore throat.
5. He will rest his voice he will be ready to sing tomorrow.
   He will rest his voice, and he will be ready to sing tomorrow.

© Evan-Moor Corp. • EMC 2754 • Language Fundamentals — Run-on Sentences 115

Page 116

Name ____________________

Sentences Review 5

Fill in the bubble next to the correct answer.

1. Which answer best corrects the run-on sentence?
   My cousins and I love to race go-karts we go every weekend.
   - Ⓐ My cousins and I love to race go-karts and we go every weekend.
   - ● My cousins and I love to race go-karts. We go every weekend.
   - Ⓒ My cousins and I love to race go-karts, we go every weekend.
   - Ⓓ My cousins and I love to race go-karts, so, we go every weekend.
2. Which answer best corrects the run-on sentence?
   I love to cook my favorite dish to cook is spaghetti.
   - ● I love to cook, and my favorite dish to cook is spaghetti.
   - Ⓑ I love to cook my favorite dish. To cook is spaghetti.
   - Ⓒ I love to cook, my favorite dish to cook is spaghetti.
   - Ⓓ I love to cook, and, my favorite dish to cook is spaghetti.
3. Which answer best corrects the run-on sentence?
   Butterflies are beautiful they don't live very long.
   - Ⓐ Butterflies are beautiful but they don't live very long.
   - Ⓑ Butterflies are beautiful They don't live very long.
   - Ⓒ Butterflies are beautiful, but, they don't live very long.
   - ● Butterflies are beautiful, but they don't live very long.
4. Which sentence is a run-on sentence?
   - ● Our school band is playing tonight it will be fun.
   - Ⓑ I practiced every day, and I improved my skills.
   - Ⓒ I will play a solo tonight. I am so excited!
   - Ⓓ Both my parents will be there to watch me play.
5. Which sentence is a run-on sentence?
   - Ⓐ I love writing stories, but it can be difficult.
   - Ⓑ I can get stuck and not be able to think of anything.
   - ● I keep writing when that happens I write anything I can imagine.
   - Ⓓ Writing anything helps with writer's block!

116 Sentences: Review 5 — Language Fundamentals • EMC 2754 • © Evan-Moor Corp.

Page 117

Name ____________________

Capitalization 1

Capitalize the first word in a sentence.

It happened a long time ago.
Do you think that one small event can change your life?

Draw three lines under the first letter of the word that needs to be capitalized.

1. the librarian wanted to buy new books for the library.
2. she thought that we needed more history books for our research projects.
3. should we get more mystery stories?
4. what about biographies?
5. my teacher would like more art books.

Write three sentences about the library. Begin them with capital letters.

6. Accept any correctly capitalized sentence.
7. ____________________
8. ____________________

© Evan-Moor Corp. • EMC 2754 • Language Fundamentals — Beginning of a Sentence 117

Page 118

Name ____________________

Capitalization 2

Capitalize the names of the days of the week and the months of the year.
On **Monday,** Mia started swimming lessons.
Her lessons will end in **July.**

Rewrite each sentence correctly.

1. on the last sunday in january, we took down wallpaper.
   On the last Sunday in January, we took down wallpaper.
2. on the first monday in february, we painted the walls.
   On the first Monday in February, we painted the walls.
3. on the second wednesday in march, we installed a new carpet.
   On the second Wednesday in March, we installed a new carpet.
4. we put up new curtains on the third friday in april.
   We put up new curtains on the third Friday in April.
5. we cleaned out the cupboards on the first saturday in may.
   We cleaned out the cupboards on the first Saturday in May.
6. last thursday, we planned our work for june.
   Last Thursday, we planned our work for June.
7. when I leave for camp on the second tuesday in july, we should be done.
   When I leave for camp on the second Tuesday in July, we should be done.
8. i will return from camp on the last saturday in august.
   I will return from camp on the last Saturday in August.

118 Days of the Week and Months of the Year — Language Fundamentals • EMC 2754 • © Evan-Moor Corp.

Page 119

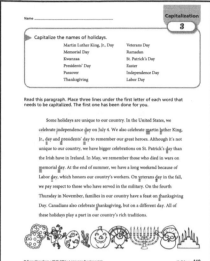

Name _____

Capitalization 3

Capitalize the names of holidays.

Martin Luther King, Jr., Day	Veterans Day
Memorial Day	Ramadan
Kwanzaa	St. Patrick's Day
Presidents' Day	Easter
Passover	Independence Day
Thanksgiving	Labor Day

Read this paragraph. Place three lines under the first letter of each word that needs to be capitalized. The first one has been done for you.

Some holidays are unique to our country. In the United States, we celebrate independence day on July 4. We also celebrate martin luther King, Jr., day and presidents' day to remember our great heroes. Although it's not unique to our country, we have bigger celebrations on St. Patrick's day than the Irish have in Ireland. In May, we remember those who died in wars on memorial day. At the end of summer, we have a long weekend because of Labor day, which honors our country's workers. On veterans day in the fall, we pay respect to those who have served in the military. On the fourth Thursday in November, families in our country have a feast on thanksgiving Day. Canadians also celebrate thanksgiving, but on a different day. All of these holidays play a part in our country's rich traditions.

© Evan-Moor Corp. • EMC 2754 • Language Fundamentals   Holidays 119

Page 120

Name _____

Capitalization Review 1

Which sentence is written correctly? Fill in the bubble next to the correct answer.

1. Ⓐ we need a lot of training to get ahead.
   ● Working very hard can help us improve.
   Ⓒ no wonder some people work so hard at their goals.
   Ⓓ success depends on many things.

2. Ⓐ On the first friday of September, we will have our first game
   Ⓑ Our last game will be on the last Saturday of october.
   ● We started practices on the third Wednesday in August.
   Ⓓ We also have practices on fridays.

3. ● Carlos's favorite holiday is Independence Day.
   Ⓑ He likes the parades on memorial Day.
   Ⓒ his second favorite holiday is Halloween.
   Ⓓ He also likes thanksgiving because of the food.

4. ● Does Rachel like to make posters?
   Ⓑ does Aidan want to enter the contest?
   Ⓒ does Maria want to paint a Thanksgiving mural?
   Ⓓ Tell mrs. carey if you would like to enter.

5. Ⓐ Kevin left on the tuesday before christmas.
   ● This year, New Year's Eve falls on a Friday.
   Ⓒ What was the forecast on groundhog day?
   Ⓓ I hope it won't be cold on st. Patrick's Day.

120 Capitalization: Review 1   Language Fundamentals • EMC 2754 • © Evan-Moor Corp.

Page 121

Name _____

Capitalization 4

Capitalize the names of people and pets.

Josh Adams got a new cat from the pound.
He named it **Buster**.
Aunt Alice got a dog named **Hodge** from the same place.

Circle the words in each sentence that need to be capitalized.

1. Uncle (joe's) favorite pet was his goldfish named (goldie.)
2. (aunt) Frieda thought (goldie) needed company.
3. She got (uncle) Joe to buy a large fish called (wendy.)
4. Miss (grace) the woman at the pet store, also showed them cats and dogs.
5. Aunt (frieda) and Uncle (joe) bought a sweet kitten.
6. Their cat (fluffy) never bothered (uncle) Joe's fish.

Write the full names of three adults whom you admire. Remember to capitalize their names.

7. _____
8. _____   Accept correctly capitalized full names.
9. _____

Write the name of a pet you have, have had, or you know. Remember to capitalize its name.

10. _____   Accept any correctly capitalized pet name.

© Evan-Moor Corp. • EMC 2754 • Language Fundamentals   Names of People and Pets 121

Page 122

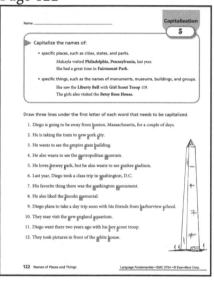

Name _____

Capitalization 5

Capitalize the names of:
- specific places, such as cities, states, and parks.
  Makayla visited **Philadelphia, Pennsylvania**, last year.
  She had a great time in **Fairmount Park**.
- specific things, such as the names of monuments, museums, buildings, and groups.
  She saw the **Liberty Bell** with **Girl Scout Troop 119**.
  The girls also visited the **Betsy Ross House**.

Draw three lines under the first letter of each word that needs to be capitalized.

1. Diego is going to be away from boston, Massachusetts, for a couple of days.
2. He is taking the train to new york city.
3. He wants to see the empire state building.
4. He also wants to see the metropolitan museum.
5. He loves fenway park, but he also wants to see yankee stadium.
6. Last year, Diego took a class trip to washington, D.C.
7. His favorite thing there was the washington monument.
8. He also liked the lincoln memorial.
9. Diego plans to take a day trip soon with his friends from harborview school.
10. They may visit the new england aquarium.
11. Diego went there two years ago with his boy scout troop.
12. They took pictures in front of the white house.

122 Names of Places and Things   Language Fundamentals • EMC 2754 • © Evan-Moor Corp.

Page 123

Name _____

Capitalization 6

Capitalize the first word and all other important words in the titles of movies, songs, and books.

Movie	The Sound of Music
Book	The Adventures of Huckleberry Finn
Song	"America the Beautiful"

Circle the words that need to be capitalized in this news article.

On Friday through Sunday, members of the Springfield Community Theater will celebrate the music of George Gershwin. Gershwin's music has been used in movies like An (american) (in) Paris and (funny face.) Many of his songs have become famous, including (i) got (rhythm) and (a foggy day.) The female soloist, Lita Williams, will sing (summertime) from the Gershwin show Porgy and (bess.) A local pianist, Emilio Blanco, will play "Rhapsody in (blue.)

Ask a friend the name of his or her favorite book. Write the title here. Remember to capitalize the important words in the title.

1. Accept any correctly capitalized title.

List the names of your three favorite movies. Use capital letters for the first word and all other important words.

2. Answers will vary. Accept any correctly capitalized
3. movie titles.
4. _____

© Evan-Moor Corp. • EMC 2754 • Language Fundamentals   Titles of Published Works 123

Page 124

Name _____

Capitalization Review 2

Which sentence uses correct capitalization? Fill in the bubble next to the correct answer.

1. Ⓐ Daphne left her cat snowball at home.
   Ⓑ Ima took her dog rex with her.
   ● Mrs. Guzman took her ferret Freddy for a walk.
   Ⓓ We wish we could bring our gerbil binky to school.

2. Ⓐ Alvin went with his family to kansas city.
   ● On the way, they drove through Davenport.
   Ⓒ After going to Kansas City, Alvin went to phoenix.
   Ⓓ Soon, he'll be back home in detroit.

3. Ⓐ My favorite book is Charlotte's Web.
   Ⓑ My favorite song is "You've got a friend."
   ● My favorite movie is The parent Trap.
   Ⓓ My favorite old TV show is the Brady bunch.

4. Ⓐ Yori flew to Chicago on new year's day.
   ● He wanted to see the sears tower.
   Ⓒ The Chicago art institute was closed.
   Ⓓ He walked all over Lincoln Park.

5. ● Did Aisha take her cat Bono to Florida?
   Ⓑ Did she go to st. Augustine?
   Ⓒ Did she travel with the wildcats, her softball team?
   Ⓓ Did they take the plane to cape canaveral?

124 Capitalization: Review 2   Language Fundamentals • EMC 2754 • © Evan-Moor Corp.

Page 125

Name _____

Abbreviations 1

An abbreviation is the shortened form of a word or group of words. Some abbreviations end in a period, but many abbreviations do not.

Word or Group of Words	Abbreviation
page	p.
Avenue	Ave.
Animal Rescue League	ARL
compact disc	CD

For each word or group of words, write the letter of the correct abbreviation on the line.

1. page ___c___   a. CIA
2. emergency medical technician ___f___   b. Ave.
3. Central Intelligence Agency ___a___   c. p.
4. National Football League ___g___   d. ASAP
5. Avenue ___b___   e. EU
6. automated teller machine ___h___   f. EMT
7. as soon as possible ___d___   g. NFL
8. European Union ___e___   h. ATM

Read each group of words. Write an abbreviation for it.
Hint: These abbreviations do not end in a period.

9. American Library Association ___ALA___
10. Public Broadcasting System ___PBS___

© Evan-Moor Corp. • EMC 2754 • Language Fundamentals   Identifying Abbreviations 125

Page 126

Name _____

Abbreviations 2

Each day of the week has an abbreviation. These abbreviations are written with a period at the end.

Day of the Week	Abbreviation
Sunday	Sun.
Monday	Mon.
Tuesday	Tue.
Wednesday	Wed.
Thursday	Thurs.
Friday	Fri.
Saturday	Sat.

Answer the following questions, using an abbreviation for one of the days of the week.

1. What is your favorite day of the week?   Answers will vary.
2. What is the first day of the school week?   Mon.
3. What is the last day of the school week?   Fri.
4. What is the first day of the weekend?   Sat.
5. On what day or days do you exercise?   Answers will vary.
6. What is the second day of the school week?   Tues.
7. What is the fourth day of the school week?   Thurs.
8. What is the day before Monday?   Sun.
9. On what day do you have the most homework?   Answers will vary.
10. What day is the middle of the school week?   Wed.

126 Days of the Week   Language Fundamentals • EMC 2754 • © Evan-Moor Corp.

Page 127

Name _____

Abbreviations 3

Most months of the year are abbreviated by using the first three letters of the name of the month, followed by a period.

Month	Abbreviation	Month	Abbreviation
January	Jan.	July	July
February	Feb.	August	Aug.
March	Mar.	September	Sept.
April	Apr.	October	Oct.
May	May	November	Nov.
June	June	December	Dec.

Use abbreviations to answer the questions about Emily's planner.

Emily's Planner

Month	Remember	Month	Remember
September:	Buy school supplies	February:	Dad's birthday
October:	Harvest Festival	March:	Visit dentist
November:	Aunt Kay's for Thanksgiving	April:	Plant flowers
December:	Mom's birthday	May:	Uncle Bo's wedding
January:	Start yoga	June:	Vacation

1. When is the Harvest Festival?   Oct.
2. What month will Emily go to Aunt Kay's?   Nov.
3. When is Emily's dad's birthday?   Feb.
4. When will Emily go to Uncle Bo's wedding?   May
5. When does school begin?   Sept.
6. Which months do not have abbreviations?   May, June, July

© Evan-Moor Corp. • EMC 2754 • Language Fundamentals   Months of the Year 127

Page 128

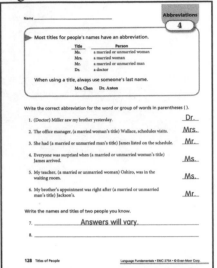

Most titles for people's names have an abbreviation.

Title	Person
Ms.	a married or unmarried woman
Mrs.	a married woman
Mr.	a married or unmarried man
Dr.	a doctor

When using a title, always use someone's last name.

Mrs. Chen   Dr. Anton

Write the correct abbreviation for the word or group of words in parentheses ( ).

1. (Doctor) Miller saw my brother yesterday.   **Dr.**

2. The office manager, (a married woman's title) Wallace, schedules visits.   **Mrs.**

3. She had (a married or unmarried man's title) James listed on the schedule.   **Mr.**

4. Everyone was surprised when (a married or unmarried woman's title) James arrived.   **Ms.**

5. My teacher, (a married or unmarried woman) Oshiro, was in the waiting room.   **Ms.**

6. My brother's appointment was right after (a married or unmarried man's title) Jackson's.   **Mr.**

Write the names and titles of two people you know.

7. _____ **Answers will vary.** _____

8. _____

128   Titles of People   Language Fundamentals • EMC 2754 • © Evan-Moor Corp.

Page 129

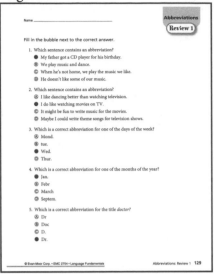

Fill in the bubble next to the correct answer.

1. Which sentence contains an abbreviation?
   - ● My father got a CD player for his birthday.
   - Ⓑ We play music and dance.
   - Ⓒ When he's not home, we play the music we like.
   - Ⓓ He doesn't like some of our music.

2. Which sentence contains an abbreviation?
   - Ⓐ I like dancing better than watching television.
   - ● I do like watching movies on TV.
   - Ⓒ It might be fun to write music for the movies.
   - Ⓓ Maybe I could write theme songs for television shows.

3. Which is a correct abbreviation for one of the days of the week?
   - Ⓐ Mond.
   - Ⓑ tue.
   - ● Wed.
   - Ⓓ Thur.

4. Which is a correct abbreviation for one of the months of the year?
   - ● Jan.
   - Ⓑ Febr
   - Ⓒ March
   - Ⓓ Septem.

5. Which is a correct abbreviation for the title *doctor*?
   - Ⓐ Dr
   - Ⓑ Doc
   - Ⓒ D.
   - ● Dr.

© Evan-Moor Corp. • EMC 2754 • Language Fundamentals   Abbreviations: Review 1   129

Page 130

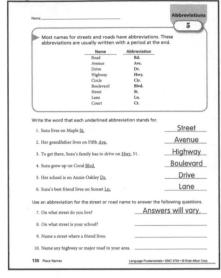

Most names for streets and roads have abbreviations. These abbreviations are usually written with a period at the end.

Name	Abbreviation
Road	Rd.
Avenue	Ave.
Drive	Dr.
Highway	Hwy.
Circle	Cir.
Boulevard	Blvd.
Street	St.
Lane	Ln.
Court	Ct.

Write the word that each underlined abbreviation stands for.

1. Suzu lives on Maple St.   **Street**

2. Her grandfather lives on Fifth Ave.   **Avenue**

3. To get there, Suzu's family has to drive on Hwy. 51.   **Highway**

4. Suzu grew up on Coral Blvd.   **Boulevard**

5. Her best friend is on Annie Oakley Dr.   **Drive**

6. Suzu's best friend lives on Sunset Ln.   **Lane**

Use an abbreviation for the street or road name to answer the following questions.

7. On what street do you live?   **Answers will vary.**

8. On what street is your school?   _____

9. Name a street where a friend lives.   _____

10. Name any highway or major road in your area.   _____

130   Place Names   Language Fundamentals • EMC 2754 • © Evan-Moor Corp.

Page 131

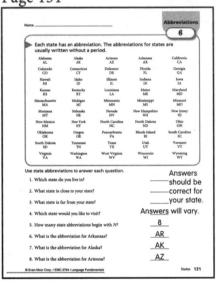

Each state has an abbreviation. The abbreviations for states are usually written without a period.

Alabama AL	Alaska AK	Arizona AZ	Arkansas AR	California CA
Colorado CO	Connecticut CT	Delaware DE	Florida FL	Georgia GA
Hawaii HI	Idaho ID	Illinois IL	Indiana IN	Iowa IA
Kansas KS	Kentucky KY	Louisiana LA	Maine ME	Maryland MD
Massachusetts MA	Michigan MI	Minnesota MN	Mississippi MS	Missouri MO
Montana MT	Nebraska NE	Nevada NV	New Hampshire NH	New Jersey NJ
New Mexico NM	New York NY	North Carolina NC	North Dakota ND	Ohio OH
Oklahoma OK	Oregon OR	Pennsylvania PA	Rhode Island RI	South Carolina SC
South Dakota SD	Tennessee TN	Texas TX	Utah UT	Vermont VT
Virginia VA	Washington WA	West Virginia WV	Wisconsin WI	Wyoming WY

Use state abbreviations to answer each question.

1. Which state do you live in?

2. What state is close to your state?

3. What state is far from your state?   **Answers should be correct for your state.**

4. Which state would you like to visit?   **Answers will vary.**

5. How many state abbreviations begin with *N*?   **8**

6. What is the abbreviation for Arkansas?   **AR**

7. What is the abbreviation for Alaska?   **AK**

8. What is the abbreviation for Arizona?   **AZ**

© Evan-Moor Corp. • EMC 2754 • Language Fundamentals   States   131

Page 132

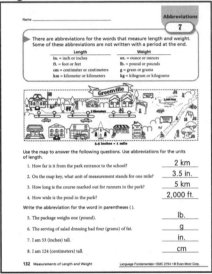

There are abbreviations for the words that measure length and weight. Some of these abbreviations are not written with a period at the end.

Length	Weight
in. = inch or inches	oz. = ounce or ounces
ft. = foot or feet	lb. = pound or pounds
cm = centimeter or centimeters	g = gram or grams
km = kilometer or kilometers	kg = kilogram or kilograms

Greenville

3.5 inch = 1 mile

Use the map to answer the following questions. Use abbreviations for the units of length.

1. How far is it from the park entrance to the school?   **2 km**

2. On the map key, what unit of measurement stands for one mile?   **3.5 in.**

3. How long is the course marked out for runners in the park?   **5 km**

4. How wide is the pond in the park?   **2,000 ft.**

Write the abbreviation for the word in parentheses ( ).

5. The package weighs one (pound).   **lb.**

6. The serving of salad dressing had four (grams) of fat.   **g**

7. I am 53 (inches) tall.   **in.**

8. I am 124 (centimeters) tall.   **cm**

132   Measurements of Length and Weight   Language Fundamentals • EMC 2754 • © Evan-Moor Corp.

Page 133

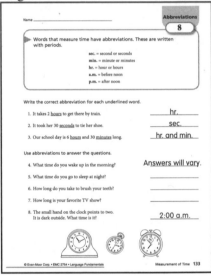

Words that measure time have abbreviations. These are written with periods.

sec. = second or seconds
min. = minute or minutes
hr. = hour or hours
a.m. = before noon
p.m. = after noon

Write the correct abbreviation for each underlined word.

1. It takes 2 hours to get there by train.   **hr.**

2. It took her 30 seconds to tie her shoe.   **sec.**

3. Our school day is 6 hours and 30 minutes long.   **hr. and min.**

Use abbreviations to answer the questions.

4. What time do you wake up in the morning?   **Answers will vary.**

5. What time do you go to sleep at night?   _____

6. How long do you take to brush your teeth?   _____

7. How long is your favorite TV show?   _____

8. The small hand on the clock points to two. It is dark outside. What time is it?   **2:00 a.m.**

© Evan-Moor Corp. • EMC 2754 • Language Fundamentals   Measurement of Time   133

Page 134

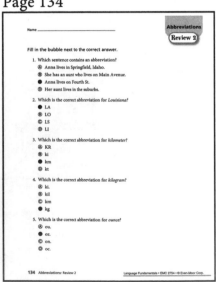

Fill in the bubble next to the correct answer.

1. Which sentence contains an abbreviation?
   - Ⓐ Anna lives in Springfield, Idaho.
   - Ⓑ She has an aunt who lives on Main Avenue.
   - ● Anna lives on Fourth St.
   - Ⓓ Her aunt lives in the suburbs.

2. Which is the correct abbreviation for *Louisiana*?
   - ● LA
   - Ⓑ LO
   - Ⓒ LS
   - Ⓓ LI

3. Which is the correct abbreviation for *kilometer*?
   - Ⓐ KR
   - Ⓑ ki
   - ● km
   - Ⓓ kt

4. Which is the correct abbreviation for *kilogram*?
   - Ⓐ ki.
   - Ⓑ kil
   - Ⓒ km
   - ● kg

5. Which is the correct abbreviation for *ounce*?
   - Ⓐ ou.
   - ● oz.
   - Ⓒ on.
   - Ⓓ oc.

134   Abbreviations: Review 2   Language Fundamentals • EMC 2754 • © Evan-Moor Corp.

Page 135

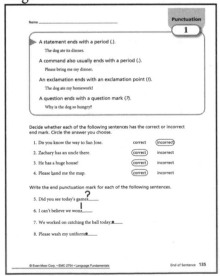

A statement ends with a period (.).
   The dog ate its dinner.

A command also usually ends with a period (.).
   Please bring me my dinner.

An exclamation ends with an exclamation point (!).
   The dog ate my homework!

A question ends with a question mark (?).
   Why is the dog so hungry?

Decide whether each of the following sentences has the correct or incorrect end mark. Circle the answer you choose.

1. Do you know the way to San Jose.   correct   (incorrect)

2. Zachary has an uncle there.   (correct)   incorrect

3. He has a huge house!   (correct)   incorrect

4. Please hand me the map.   (correct)   incorrect

Write the end punctuation mark for each of the following sentences.

5. Did you see today's game **?**

6. I can't believe we won **!**

7. We worked on catching the ball today **.**

8. Please wash my uniform **.**

© Evan-Moor Corp. • EMC 2754 • Language Fundamentals   End of Sentence   135

Page 136

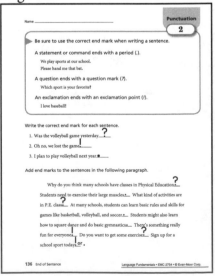

Be sure to use the correct end mark when writing a sentence.

A statement or command ends with a period (.).
   We play sports at our school.
   Please hand me that bat.

A question ends with a question mark (?).
   Which sport is your favorite?

An exclamation ends with an exclamation point (!).
   I love baseball!

Write the correct end mark for each sentence.

1. Was the volleyball game yesterday **?**

2. Oh no, we lost the game **!**

3. I plan to play volleyball next year **.**

Add end marks to the sentences in the following paragraph.

Why do you think many schools have classes in Physical Education **?** Students need to exercise their large muscles **.** What kind of activities are in P.E. class **?** At many schools, students can learn basic rules and skills for games like basketball, volleyball, and soccer **.** Students might also learn how to square dance and do basic gymnastics **.** There's something really fun for everyone **.** Do you want to get some exercise **?** Sign up for a school sport today **!**

136   End of Sentence   Language Fundamentals • EMC 2754 • © Evan-Moor Corp.

Page 137

Name _____

Which sentence has the correct end punctuation?
Fill in the bubble next to the correct answer.

1. Are music lessons good for students.
   - Ⓐ Lusita takes guitar lessons.
   - Ⓑ She says that guitar lessons are great?
   - Ⓒ Lusita really likes her lessons

2. Ⓐ Which do you like better, piano or guitar!
   - Ⓑ Bao takes piano lessons!
   - Ⓒ Piano lessons are terrific!
   - Ⓓ Bao's father is glad Bao is getting lessons!

3. Ⓐ Do you like all kinds of music?
   - Ⓑ Kaitlyn likes playing pop songs?
   - Ⓒ She says, "They rock!"
   - Ⓓ Kaitlyn also likes classical music

4. Ⓐ Ms. Desai teaches music at school.
   - Ⓑ She says it's really fun?
   - Ⓒ I want to teach music when I grow up
   - Ⓓ Ms. Desai told me to work hard!

5. Ⓐ Drums are my favorite instrument
   - Ⓑ Ms. Mack plays drums
   - Ⓒ Do you like drums, too.
   - Ⓓ They're really loud!

Page 138

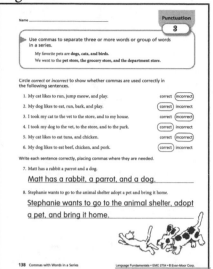

Name _____

Use commas to separate three or more words or group of words in a series.
My favorite pets are dogs, cats, and birds.
We went to the pet store, the grocery store, and the department store.

Circle correct or incorrect to show whether commas are used correctly in the following sentences.

1. My cat likes to run, jump meow, and play.   correct (incorrect)
2. My dog likes to eat, run, bark, and play.   correct   incorrect
3. I took my cat to the vet to the store, and to my house. correct (incorrect)
4. I took my dog to the vet, to the store, and to the park. (correct) incorrect
5. My cat likes to eat tuna, and chicken.   correct (incorrect)
6. My dog likes to eat beef, chicken, and pork.   (correct) incorrect

Write each sentence correctly, placing commas where they are needed.

7. Matt has a rabbit a parrot and a dog.

   Matt has a rabbit, a parrot, and a dog.

8. Stephanie wants to go to the animal shelter adopt a pet and bring it home.

   Stephanie wants to go to the animal shelter, adopt a pet, and bring it home.

Page 139

Name _____

Use commas to separate three or more words or group of words in a series.
Jasmine has to do writing, reading, and math before bedtime.
Dylan needs to wash the dishes, take out the trash, and do his homework before bedtime.

Add commas where they belong in each series.

1. I studied last night with Lesh, Bryan, and Sean.
2. We worked on math, reading, and spelling.
3. Afterwards, I watched TV, ate dessert, and went to bed.
4. This morning, I got up, got dressed, and went to school.
5. I have a peanut butter sandwich, a box of raisins, and a bag of carrots for lunch.
6. After school, do you want to stay home, go to the parlor, go to Eric's house?
7. If you stay home, will you do chores, do your homework, or play video games?
8. For dinner, I had fish, rice, green beans, and salad.
9. Before bed, I took a bath, brushed my teeth, and read a book.

Write a sentence about what you did last night. Use three or more words or groups of words in a series. Remember to place commas where they belong.

10. _____ **Answers will vary.** _____

Page 140

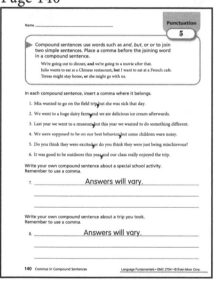

Name _____

Compound sentences use words such as and, but, or or to join two simple sentences. Place a comma before the joining word in a compound sentence.
We're going out to dinner, and we're going to a movie after that.
Julio wants to eat at a Chinese restaurant, but I want to eat at a French cafe.
Teresa might stay home, or she might go with us.

In each compound sentence, insert a comma where it belongs.

1. Mia wanted to go on the field trip, but she was sick that day.
2. We went to a huge dairy farm, and we ate delicious ice cream afterwards.
3. Last year we went to a museum, but this year we wanted to do something different.
4. We were supposed to be on our best behavior, but some children were noisy.
5. Do you think they were excited, or do you think they were just being mischievous?
6. It was good to be outdoors this year, and our class really enjoyed the trip.

Write your own compound sentence about a special school activity. Remember to use a comma.

7. _____ **Answers will vary.** _____

Write your own compound sentence about a trip you took. Remember to use a comma.

8. _____ **Answers will vary.** _____

Page 141

Name _____

A complex sentence uses words such as although, because, when, since, and while to join two related sentences. If the joining word comes at the beginning of the sentence, use a comma between the two sentences.
Although I liked the gift, I thought my aunt spent too much money on it.

For each sentence, insert a comma if one is needed.

1. Although I am younger than my sister, I am older than my brother Max.
2. Because I am older than Max, he wants to be like me.
3. When he gets to be my age, he'll probably feel different about it.
4. While Max looks up to me, I look up to my sister Jessica.
5. Although it might not mean much to her, I like to go to all of her softball games.
6. Since she's the oldest, Jessica is our role model.

Write two complex sentences about the members of your family. Start your sentences with although, while, when, or because. Remember to use a comma to separate the two sentences when you join them.

7. _____ **Accept any reasonable answer.** _____

8. _____

Page 142

Name _____

Which sentence is written correctly?
Fill in the bubble next to the correct answer.

1. Ⓐ The room was crowded with chairs sofas and tables.
   - Ⓑ We sold dishes old clothes and furniture at our garage sale.
   - Ⓒ My brother my sister and my mother all worked hard.
   - Ⓓ Neighbors, strangers, and friends all came to the sale.

2. Ⓐ Kevin walked to the bus stop got on the bus and got off at school.
   - Ⓑ He went to his first class, went to his second class, and then went to P.E.
   - Ⓒ In P.E., he practiced running dribbling a ball and passing.
   - Ⓓ After P.E., he went to math class then social studies and then the lunchroom.

3. Ⓐ Sonia tried out for the school play, and she got the biggest part.
   - Ⓑ She is really good at acting but it's hard to hear her voice.
   - Ⓒ Will people enjoy the show or will they be bored?
   - Ⓓ Sonia has been practicing speaking loudly, and, she's much easier to hear.

4. Ⓐ Although Ahmed likes science he likes art best of all.
   - Ⓑ While, some enjoy painting still life, he prefers painting portraits.
   - Ⓒ Although he is young, his artwork is very advanced.
   - Ⓓ While no one else was surprised Ahmed was amazed when he won the contest.

5. Ⓐ Although Serena loves theater she is really best at writing.
   - Ⓑ When everyone read her story they recognized her talent.
   - Ⓒ While Serena works at writing, her sister works at acting.
   - Ⓓ When they grow up they may choose other careers.

Page 143

Name _____

Use a comma between the day and the year in a date.
July 4, 1865
February 18, 2010

Rewrite each sentence. Add commas where they are needed.

1. My sister was born on November 12 2006.

   My sister was born on November 12, 2006.

2. My mother and father got married on June 18 1996.

   My mother and father got married on June 18, 1996.

3. We are having a party for my grandmother on September 14 2008.

   We are having a party for my grandmother on September 14, 2008.

4. She turns 65 on September 10 2008.

   She turns 65 on September 10, 2008.

5. I met my best friend on September 1 2005.

   I met my best friend on September 1, 2005.

6. She was born on June 9 2000.

   She was born on June 9, 2000.

Page 144

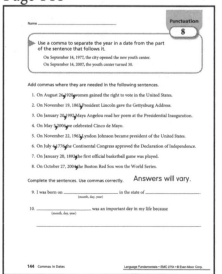

Name _____

Use a comma to separate the year in a date from the part of the sentence that follows it.
On September 14, 1977, the city opened the new youth center.
On September 14, 2007, the youth center turned 30.

Add commas where they are needed in the following sentences.

1. On August 26, 1920, women gained the right to vote in the United States.
2. On November 19, 1863, President Lincoln gave the Gettysburg Address.
3. On January 20, 1993, Maya Angelou read her poem at the Presidential Inauguration.
4. On May 5, 2006, we celebrated Cinco de Mayo.
5. On November 22, 1963, Lyndon Johnson became president of the United States.
6. On July 4, 1776, the Continental Congress approved the Declaration of Independence.
7. On January 20, 1892, the first official basketball game was played.
8. On October 27, 2004, the Boston Red Sox won the World Series.

Complete the sentences. Use commas correctly.   **Answers will vary.**

9. I was born on _____ in the state of _____
   (month, day, year)

10. _____ was an important day in my life because
    (month, day, year)

Page 145

Name _____

When writing someone's address on an envelope, use a comma between the name of the city and the state abbreviation.

Madison Lincoln   Melissa Hampton
1010 Fifth Street   222 Bellvista Road
Albany, NY 12203   St. Louis, MO 63108

Add commas where they are needed to the addresses below.

1. Ben MacMillan   2. Yolanda Williams   3. Ms. Patty Street
   34 Pinetree Lane   17 Central Street   42 Mandolin Lane
   Concord, NH 03201   New Haven, CT 06610   Orlando, FL 32205

4. Laura Sanchez   5. Mr. Mark Lieu   6. Roberto Carmina
   4070 Main Street   3820 28th Street   14820 Atlantic Avenue
   Cleveland, OH 44202   San Francisco, CA 94431 Leonia, NJ 07205

Write your address below. Remember to use a comma where it belongs.

Answers will vary. Accept any correctly punctuated address.

Page 146

Punctuation **10**

▶ Use a comma to separate the name of a city from the name of a state, province, or country.

The temperature was hot in Phoenix, Arizona.

Use a comma to separate the name of a state, province, or country from the part of the sentence that follows it.

The temperature in Montreal, Quebec, was really cold.
In Paris, France, the weather was rainy.

Add commas where they belong.

1. In Detroit, Michigan, many cars are made.
2. In Gettysburg, Pennsylvania, many apples are grown.
3. There are great jobs in Dublin, Ireland, for people who live there.
4. When I went to Savannah, Georgia, I saw peach trees.
5. In Sydney, Australia, there is a great opera house.
6. We went to San Diego, California, on spring break.
7. In Toronto, Ontario, we went to a film festival.
8. The Olympics in Salt Lake City, Utah, were very exciting.
9. In Austin, Texas, we heard fantastic music.
10. I want to go to Cairo, Egypt, someday.

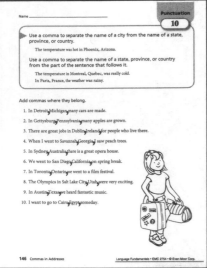

Page 147

Punctuation **11**

▶ Use a comma after the greeting in a friendly letter.

Dear Aunt Margaret,
Dear Lupe,

Use a comma after the closing in any letter.

Sincerely,
Love,

Read these letters. Insert commas where they belong.

Dear Mom,
You were right. Summer camp is really fun!
Love,
Kim

Dear Ms. Lawson,
Thank you for looking after Snuffles while we were gone. That was very nice of you.
Sincerely,
Janie Lampert

Dear Paris,
Thanks for the tickets. The show was awesome!
Your cousin,
Frankie

Dear Grandma,
I can't wait to see you next summer! I hope we can go swimming together again.
Love,
Zoe

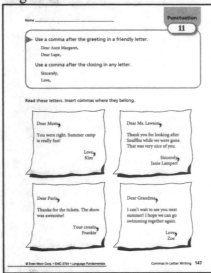

Page 148

Punctuation **12**

▶ Use a comma to separate the name of the person being addressed from the rest of the sentence.

Lucia, where did you get those roller skates?
What are you doing tonight, Max?

Write these sentences correctly by adding commas where they are needed.

1. Jacob would you please grab the paintbrush?

Jacob, would you please grab the paintbrush?

2. Is it time for your lesson Haley?

Is it time for your lesson, Haley?

3. Mom I want a birthday party, please.

Mom, I want a birthday party, please.

4. Ms. Iyo I won't be in school tomorrow.

Ms. Iyo, I won't be in school tomorrow.

5. Auntie Roseann would you sign this form for our field trip?

Auntie Roseann, would you sign this form for our field trip?

6. What was it like when you were in fourth grade Grandpa?

What was it like when you were in fourth grade, Grandpa?

Page 149

Punctuation **Review 3**

Fill in the bubble next to the correct answer.

1. Which sentence is written correctly?
   Ⓐ Mrs. Gallagher's son was born on May 7, 2004.
   Ⓑ Her daughter was born on October 15 2006.
   Ⓒ Mrs. Gallagher was born on November, 27 1980.
   Ⓓ On September 2 1985 she started kindergarten.

2. Which sentence is written correctly?
   Ⓐ On September 10, 2005 the school celebrated its 50th anniversary.
   Ⓑ On September 10, 1955, the school was a very different place.
   Ⓒ By September 12 1980 the number of students had doubled.
   Ⓓ On October 5 2005, we will hold a reunion.

3. Which sentence is written correctly?
   Ⓐ In Alexandria, Virginia, there are many historical places to visit.
   Ⓑ When we went to Seattle Washington we saw Pioneer Square.
   Ⓒ In Portland, Oregon we went to coffee houses.
   Ⓓ In St. Paul Minnesota we went to the symphony.

4. Which greeting for a friendly letter is written correctly?
   Ⓐ Dear Jackson
   Ⓑ Dear, Mackenzie
   Ⓒ Dear Alejandro:
   Ⓓ Dear Molly,

5. Which sentence is written correctly?
   Ⓐ Can I borrow your pink sweater Erin?
   Ⓑ Paige I think, you lost that sweater.
   Ⓒ Erin, you must have something else I can wear.
   Ⓓ Paige I really don't think that I do.

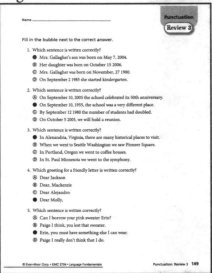

Page 150

Punctuation **13**

▶ Use commas to separate quotations—the exact words someone says—from the rest of the sentence.

If the comma comes after the quotation, place the comma before the ending quotation mark.

Hunter said, "I have to sell some wrapping paper for the school fundraiser."
"I'll buy three rolls," Hunter's aunt replied.

These sentences contain dialogue. Add commas where they belong.

1. Maria asked, "What club do you want to join?"
2. "I want to join the chess club," Melanie said.
3. "I don't know how to play chess," Ian said.
4. "We could join the reading group," Melanie said.
5. Maria said, "I'm not sure."
6. "I am," Ian replied.
7. "I'd like to be on a sports team," Koji said.
8. Maria said, "I'd really love to be in the choir."
9. "I would, too," Ian answered.
10. "I guess we'll do different things," Koji said.
11. "That's okay," said Maria.
12. "We will see each other in class," agreed Ian.

Page 151

Punctuation **14**

▶ Use quotation marks to separate the exact words someone says.

"We went straight from winter to summer this year," said Olivia.
Soon Li replied, "That is putting it mildly!"

Rewrite each sentence, placing quotation marks where they belong.

1. Ava said, My little brother and I went to the dentist today.

Ava said, "My little brother and I went to the dentist today."

2. Floss your teeth, said Dr. Smith.

"Floss your teeth," said Dr. Smith.

3. The dentist gave me floss, said Ava.

"The dentist gave me floss," said Ava.

4. Ava said, The dentist told me I was a good sport.

Ava said, "The dentist told me I was a good sport."

Rewrite each sentence correctly.

5. It's great to be able to speak more than one language said Mason.

"It's great to be able to speak more than one language." said Mason.

6. Luis replied I speak English and Spanish.

Luis replied, "I speak English and Spanish."

Page 152

Punctuation **15**

▶ If a quotation is interrupted by words telling who is speaking, use quotation marks to set off the speaker's exact words.

"It's hot in here," said Elijah, "and I'll be happy to get outside."

Rewrite each sentence correctly. Remember to use quotation marks.

1. I like to eat pizza, said Ethan, but not every day.

"I like to eat pizza," said Ethan, "but not every day."

2. I'd rather eat pasta, said Ashley, as long as there are meatballs.

"I'd rather eat pasta," said Ashley, "as long as there are meatballs."

3. If I could cook, said Juan, I'd eat steak every day.

"If I could cook," said Juan, "I'd eat steak every day."

4. My mother says if I learn to cook, said Ashley, I might stop being so picky.

"My mother says if I learn to cook," said Ashley, "I might stop being so picky."

5. I want to be a great cook someday, said Ethan, so I can just eat what I want.

"I want to be a great cook someday," said Ethan, "so I can just eat what I want."

Page 153

Punctuation **16**

▶ Use quotation marks around the titles of short stories, poems, and songs.

"Apple Blossoms"   "Jellyfish Stew"   "Rosalita"

Write each of the following titles correctly. Remember to use quotation marks.

1. (short story) How the Alphabet Was Made

"How the Alphabet Was Made"

2. (poem) The Raven

"The Raven"

3. (song) This Land Is Your Land

"This Land Is Your Land"

Write an answer to each question. Remember to use quotation marks correctly.

4. What is your favorite song?

Accept any correctly punctuated song title.

5. What is your favorite short story?

Accept any correctly punctuated short story title.

6. What is your favorite poem?

Accept any correctly punctuated poem title.

Page 154

Punctuation **17**

▶ Underline the titles of books, movies, television shows, newspapers, and magazines.

The Trumpet of the Swan
Aladdin
Lizzie Maguire
The Sacramento Bee
Highlights for Children

If you are using a computer, use *italics* for titles.

The Trumpet of the Swan by E. B. White   *Highlights for Children*

Correct the following paragraph. Remember to underline the titles of movies, books, newspapers, magazines, and television shows.

My favorite movie is Nanny McPhee. I read an article about it in the Springfield Times and couldn't wait to see it. Then I read more about it in Newsweek. I thought Emma Thompson was fantastic playing the part of the nanny. That made me curious about what else she had done. I looked to see if she was ever on television. Funnily enough, she played a children's entertainer on the old TV show Cheers, and her character's name was Nanny G. I thought that Emma Thompson was terrific in this movie!

Answer the question with a complete sentence.

What book are you reading now?

Accept any correctly punctuated title.

Page 155

Review 4

Fill in the bubble next to the correct answer.

1. Which sentence is written correctly?
   - Ⓐ Mrs. Gomez said "I think it's time to go home.
   - Ⓑ Her daughter said, "I don't want to go."
   - Ⓒ Mrs. Gomez said, "We're all getting hungry."
   - Ⓓ That's true said her daughter.

2. Which sentence is written correctly?
   - Ⓐ Alexis told me that "spring is her favorite season."
   - Ⓑ Jose said, "I prefer summer."
   - Ⓒ Julia said, "I like winter."
   - Ⓓ Kyle said, I like fall.

3. Which sentence is written correctly?
   - Ⓐ "I can't decide, said Morgan "what I want to be when I grow up."
   - Ⓑ "The problem is," said Jackson, you have too many choices."
   - Ⓒ "I think," said Morgan, "that you may be right."
   - Ⓓ Of course, said Jackson, I'm always right.

4. Which short story title is written correctly?
   - Ⓐ The Brief Adventures of a Small Mouse
   - Ⓑ *The Brief Adventures of a Small Mouse*
   - Ⓒ The Brief Adventures of a Small Mouse
   - Ⓓ "The Brief Adventures of a Small Mouse"

5. Which book title is written correctly?
   - Ⓐ The Beastly Feast
   - Ⓑ "The Beastly Feast"
   - Ⓒ *The Beastly Feast*
   - Ⓓ The Beastly "Feast"

Page 156

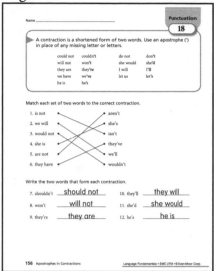

18

A contraction is a shortened form of two words. Use an apostrophe (') in place of any missing letter or letters.

could not	couldn't	do not	don't
will not	won't	she would	she'd
they are	they're	I will	I'll
we have	we've	let us	let's
he is	he's		

Match each set of two words to the correct contraction.

1. is not — isn't
2. we will — we'll
3. would not — wouldn't
4. she is — she's
5. are not — aren't
6. they have — they've

Write the two words that form each contraction.

7. shouldn't — should not
8. won't — will not
9. they're — they are
10. they'll — they will
11. she'd — she would
12. he's — he is

Page 157

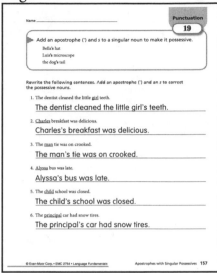

19

Add an apostrophe (') and s to a singular noun to make it possessive.

Bella's hat
Luis's microscope
the dog's tail

Rewrite the following sentences. Add an apostrophe (') and an s to correct the possessive nouns.

1. The dentist cleaned the little girl teeth.
   The dentist cleaned the little girl's teeth.

2. Charles breakfast was delicious.
   Charles's breakfast was delicious.

3. The man tie was on crooked.
   The man's tie was on crooked.

4. Alyssa bus was late.
   Alyssa's bus was late.

5. The child school was closed.
   The child's school was closed.

6. The principal car had snow tires.
   The principal's car had snow tires.

Page 158

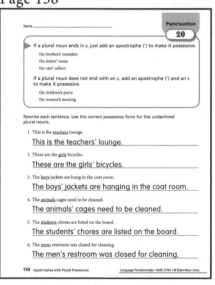

20

If a plural noun ends in s, just add an apostrophe (') to make it possessive.

the brothers' mistakes
the sisters' room
the cats' collars

If a plural noun does not end with an s, add an apostrophe (') and an s to make it possessive.

the children's party
the women's meeting

Rewrite each sentence. Use the correct possessive form for the underlined plural nouns.

1. This is the teachers lounge.
   This is the teachers' lounge.

2. These are the girls bicycles.
   These are the girls' bicycles.

3. The boys jackets are hung in the coat room.
   The boys' jackets are hanging in the coat room.

4. The animals cages need to be cleaned.
   The animals' cages need to be cleaned.

5. The students chores are listed on the board.
   The students' chores are listed on the board.

6. The mens restroom was closed for cleaning.
   The men's restroom was closed for cleaning.

Page 159

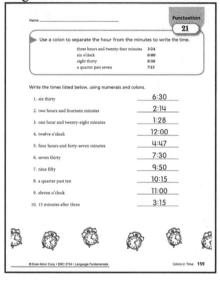

21

Use a colon to separate the hour from the minutes to write the time.

three hours and twenty-four minutes	3:24
six o'clock	6:00
eight thirty	8:30
a quarter past seven	7:15

Write the times listed below, using numerals and colons.

1. six thirty — 6:30
2. two hours and fourteen minutes — 2:14
3. one hour and twenty-eight minutes — 1:28
4. twelve o'clock — 12:00
5. four hours and forty-seven minutes — 4:47
6. seven thirty — 7:30
7. nine fifty — 9:50
8. a quarter past ten — 10:15
9. eleven o'clock — 11:00
10. 15 minutes after three — 3:15

Page 160

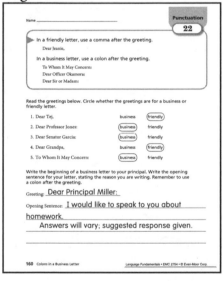

22

In a friendly letter, use a comma after the greeting.

Dear Jeanie,

In a business letter, use a colon after the greeting.

To Whom It May Concern:
Dear Officer Okamora:
Dear Sir or Madam:

Read the greetings below. Circle whether the greetings are for a business or friendly letter.

1. Dear Tej, — business — (friendly)
2. Dear Professor Jones: — (business) — friendly
3. Dear Senator Garcia: — (business) — friendly
4. Dear Grandpa, — business — (friendly)
5. To Whom It May Concern: — (business) — friendly

Write the beginning of a business letter to your principal. Write the opening sentence for your letter, stating the reason you are writing. Remember to use a colon after the greeting.

Greeting: Dear Principal Miller:

Opening Sentence: I would like to speak to you about homework.

Answers will vary; suggested response given.

Page 161

Review 5

Fill in the bubble next to the correct answer.

1. Which contraction is written correctly?
   - Ⓐ dont
   - Ⓑ shes'
   - Ⓒ theyll
   - Ⓓ didn't

2. Which singular possessive is written correctly?
   - Ⓐ Josés house
   - Ⓑ Shawnas' toy
   - Ⓒ Jason's journey
   - Ⓓ Colins book

3. Which plural possessive is written correctly?
   - Ⓐ the dogs breakfast
   - Ⓑ the children's workshop
   - Ⓒ the ladies purses
   - Ⓓ the cats's purring

4. Which time is written correctly?
   - Ⓐ 1015
   - Ⓑ 10:15
   - Ⓒ 10/fifteen
   - Ⓓ ten 15

5. Which greeting is written correctly for a business letter?
   - Ⓐ Dear John,
   - Ⓑ Dear Sir
   - Ⓒ Dear Mr. Bailey
   - Ⓓ Dear Mr. Bailey:

Page 162

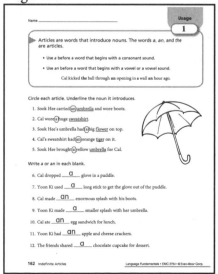

Usage 1

Articles are words that introduce nouns. The words a, an, and the are articles.

- Use a before a word that begins with a consonant sound.
- Use an before a word that begins with a vowel or a vowel sound.

Cal kicked the ball through an opening in a wall an hour ago.

Circle each article. Underline the noun it introduces.

1. Sook Hee carried an umbrella and wore boots.
2. Cal wore a huge sweatshirt.
3. Sook Hee's umbrella had a big flower on top.
4. Cal's sweatshirt had an orange tiger on it.
5. Sook Hee brought a yellow umbrella for Cal.

Write a or an in each blank.

6. Cal dropped __a__ glove in a puddle.
7. Yoon Ki used __a__ long stick to get the glove out of the puddle.
8. Cal made __an__ enormous splash with his boots.
9. Yoon Ki made __a__ smaller splash with her umbrella.
10. Cal ate __an__ egg sandwich for lunch.
11. Yoon Ki had __an__ apple and cheese crackers.
12. The friends shared __a__ chocolate cupcake for dessert.

Page 163

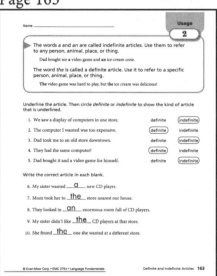

Usage 2

The words a and an are called indefinite articles. Use them to refer to any person, animal, place, or thing.

Dad bought me a video game and an ice-cream cone.

The word the is called a definite article. Use it to refer to a specific person, animal, place, or thing.

The video game was hard to play, but the ice cream was delicious!

Underline the article. Then circle *definite* or *indefinite* to show the kind of article that is underlined.

1. We saw a display of computers in one store. — definite — (indefinite)
2. The computer I wanted was too expensive. — (definite) — indefinite
3. Dad took me to an old store downtown. — definite — (indefinite)
4. They had the same computer! — (definite) — indefinite
5. Dad bought it and a video game for himself. — definite — (indefinite)

Write the correct article in each blank.

6. My sister wanted __a__ new CD player.
7. Mom took her to __the__ store nearest our house.
8. They looked in __an__ enormous room full of CD players.
9. My sister didn't like __the__ CD players at that store.
10. She found __the__ one she wanted at a different store.

Page 164

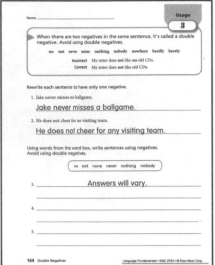

When there are two negatives in the same sentence, it's called a double negative. Avoid using double negatives.

no   not   never   none   nothing   nobody   nowhere   hardly   barely

Incorrect   My sister does **not** like **no** old CDs.
Correct   My sister does **not** like old CDs.

Rewrite each sentence to have only one negative.

1. Jake never misses no ballgame.

   Jake never misses a ballgame.

2. He does not cheer for no visiting team.

   He does not cheer for any visiting team.

Using words from the word box, write sentences using negatives.
Avoid using double negatives.

no   not   never   nothing   nobody

3. _____ **Answers will vary.** _____

4. _____

5. _____

164   Double Negatives   Language Fundamentals • EMC 2754 • © Evan-Moor Corp.

Page 165

It is easy to confuse words such as *good, well, bad,* and *badly.*

• *Good* is an adjective. Use *good* to describe nouns.
• *Well* is usually an adverb. Use *well* to describe action verbs.
  Irma plays the piano **well**. She is a **good** pianist.
• *Bad* is an adjective. Use *bad* to describe nouns.
• *Badly* is an adverb. Use *badly* to describe action verbs.
  Kasey sings very **badly**. She is a **bad** singer.

Write *good* or *well* to describe each underlined word.

1. Pam makes ____**good**____ pasta sauce.

2. She uses ____**good**____ tomatoes and onions.

3. She stirs the mixture ____**well**____ as it cooks.

4. Dad told Pam that she did very ____**well**____

5. Mom says that no one makes pasta sauce as ____**good**____ as Pam's.

Write *bad* or *badly* to describe each underlined word.

6. Jiro skates very ____**badly**____

7. He makes very ____**bad**____ spins.

8. He jumps ____**badly**____, too.

9. He wears a ____**bad**____ costume.

10. He performs ____**badly**____ at every contest.

Using Good and Well; Bad and Badly   165

Page 166

Fill in the bubble next to the correct answer.

1. Choose the article that belongs in the blank.
   Be sure to take _____ umbrella when it's raining.
   Ⓐ a
   ● an
   Ⓒ am
   Ⓓ and

2. Choose the definite article.
   Ⓐ a
   Ⓑ an
   ● the
   Ⓓ some

3. Which sentence is written correctly?
   Ⓐ No one can't beat me at chess.
   Ⓑ Randy never makes no home runs.
   ● Neka never brings an apple in her lunch.
   Ⓓ Our teacher doesn't give us no homework on Fridays.

4. Which sentence is written correctly?
   ● Mom puts nothing on her toast.
   Ⓑ Mom never puts nothing on her toast.
   Ⓒ Mom does not put nothing on her toast.
   Ⓓ Mom does not never put anything on her toast.

5. Which sentence is written correctly?
   Ⓐ Liz kicks very good.
   ● Liz plays hockey well.
   Ⓒ Liz plays a well game.
   Ⓓ Liz can pass the ball good.

166   Usage: Review 1   Language Fundamentals • EMC 2754 • © Evan-Moor Corp.

Page 167

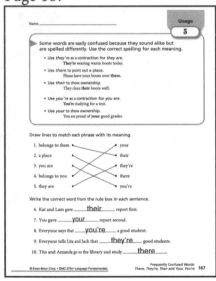

Some words are easily confused because they sound alike but are spelled differently. Use the correct spelling for each meaning.

• Use *they're* as a contraction for *they are.*
  They're wearing warm boots today.
• Use *there* to point out a place.
  Please leave your boots over **there**.
• Use *their* to show ownership.
  They clean **their** boots well.

• Use *you're* as a contraction for *you are.*
  You're studying for a test.
• Use *your* to show ownership.
  You are proud of **your** good grades.

Draw lines to match each phrase with its meaning.

1. belongs to them   your
2. a place   their
3. you are   they're
4. belongs to you   there
5. they are   you're

Write the correct word from the rule box in each sentence.

6. Kat and Lam gave ____**their**____ report first.

7. You gave ____**your**____ report second.

8. Everyone says that ____**you're**____ a good student.

9. Everyone tells Lita and Jack that ____**they're**____ good students.

10. Tito and Amanda go to the library and study ____**there**____

Frequently Confused Words:
There, They're, Their and Your, You're   167

Page 168

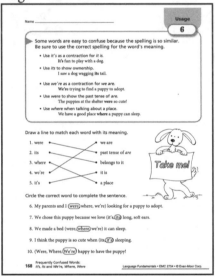

Some words are easy to confuse because the spelling is so similar. Be sure to use the correct spelling for the word's meaning.

• Use *it's* as a contraction for *it is.*
  It's fun to play with a dog.
• Use *its* to show ownership.
  I saw a dog wagging **its** tail.
• Use *we're* as a contraction for *we are.*
  We're trying to find a puppy to adopt.
• Use *were* to show the past tense of *are.*
  The puppies at the shelter **were** so cute!
• Use *where* when talking about a place.
  We have a good place **where** a puppy can sleep.

Draw a line to match each word with its meaning.

1. were   we are
2. its   past tense of *are*
3. where   belongs to it
4. we're   it is
5. it's   a place

Take me!

Circle the correct word to complete the sentence.

6. My parents and I (were) where, we're) looking for a puppy to adopt.

7. We chose this puppy because we love (it's,(its)) long, soft ears.

8. We made a bed (were,(where) we're) it can sleep.

9. I think the puppy is so cute when (its,(it's)) sleeping.

10. (Were, Where,(We're)) happy to have the puppy!

Frequently Confused Words:
168   It's, Its and We're, Where, Were   Language Fundamentals • EMC 2754 • © Evan-Moor Corp.

Page 169

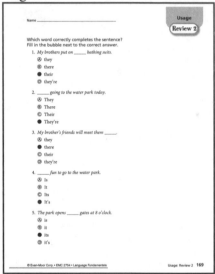

Which word correctly completes the sentence?
Fill in the bubble next to the correct answer.

1. *My brothers put on _____ bathing suits.*
   Ⓐ they
   Ⓑ there
   ● their
   Ⓓ they're

2. *_____ going to the water park today.*
   Ⓐ They
   Ⓑ There
   Ⓒ Their
   ● They're

3. *My brother's friends will meet them _____.*
   Ⓐ they
   ● there
   Ⓒ their
   Ⓓ they're

4. *_____ fun to go to the water park.*
   Ⓐ Is
   ● It
   Ⓒ Its
   Ⓓ It's

5. *The park opens _____ gates at 8 o'clock.*
   Ⓐ is
   Ⓑ it
   ● its
   Ⓓ it's

Usage: Review 2   169

Page 170

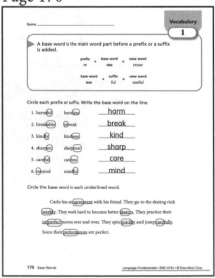

A base word is the main word part before a prefix or a suffix is added.

| prefix | + | base word | = | new word |
| re | | use | | reuse |

| base word | + | suffix | = | new word |
| use | | ful | | useful |

Circle each prefix or suffix. Write the base word on the line.

1. harm(ful)   harm(less)   **harm**
2. break(able)   (re)break   **break**
3. kind(ly)   kind(ness)   **kind**
4. sharp(en)   sharp(ener)   **sharp**
5. care(ful)   care(less)   **care**
6. (re)mind   mind(ful)   **mind**

Circle the base word in each underlined word.

Carlo has an (agree)ment with his friend. They go to the skating rink (week)ly. They work hard to become better (skat)ers. They practice their (im)perfect moves over and over. They spin (quick)ly and jump (care)fully. Soon their (perform)ances are perfect.

170   Base Words   Language Fundamentals • EMC 2754 • © Evan-Moor Corp.

Page 171

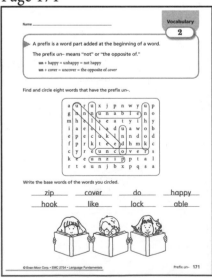

A prefix is a word part added at the beginning of a word.

The prefix *un–* means "not" or "the opposite of."

un + happy = unhappy = not happy
un + cover = uncover = the opposite of *cover*

Find and circle eight words that have the prefix *un–*.

a	u	r	x	j	p	n	w	y	u	p
g	n	n	(u	n	a	b	l	e)	n	o
m	h	a	(s	e	a	t	y	i	h	y
l	a	e	o	(u	a	d	u	a	w)	o
e	p	e	c	u	k	l	n	n	d	o
f	p	r	k	t	e	e	d	h	m	k
c	y	r	e	(u	n	c	o	v	e	r)
k	e	e	(u	n	z	i	p)	p	t	a
r	t	e	u	n	j	b	x	p	q	s

Write the base words of the words you circled.

| ___**zip**___ | ___**cover**___ | ___**do**___ | ___**happy**___ |
| ___**hook**___ | ___**like**___ | ___**lock**___ | ___**able**___ |

Prefix un–   171

Page 172

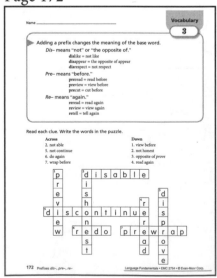

Adding a prefix changes the meaning of the base word.

Dis– means "not" or "the opposite of."
  dislike = not like
  disappear = the opposite of appear
  disrespect = not respect

Pre– means "before."
  preread = read before
  preview = view before
  precut = cut before

Re– means "again."
  reread = read again
  review = view again
  retell = tell again

Read each clue. Write the words in the puzzle.

Across
2. not able
5. not continue
6. do again
7. wrap before

Down
1. view before
2. opposite of *prove*
3. not honest
4. read again

Crossword answers:
3 (Across) d i s a b l e
d i s c o n t i n u e
r e d o   p r e w r a p

172   Prefixes dis–, pre–, re–   Language Fundamentals • EMC 2754 • © Evan-Moor Corp.

Page 173

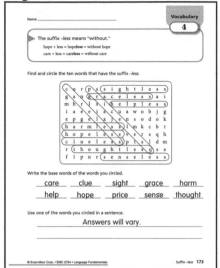

Name _____

Vocabulary 4

The suffix *-less* means "without."

hope + less = hopeless = without hope
care + less = careless = without care

Find and circle the ten words that have the suffix *-less*.

```
c u r p s s i g h t l e s s
g a n g r a c e l e s s a i
m h r l s i h e l p l e s s
i a e e i a c u a w o b j g
e p g e l e n s o d o k
h a r m l e s s l m k c b t
h o p e l e s s y e r s q h
c l u e l e s s p s l d m
r t h o u g h t l e s s s e
f l p n r s e n s e l e s s
```

Write the base words of the words you circled.

| care | clue | sight | grace | harm |
| help | hope | price | sense | thought |

Use one of the words you circled in a sentence.

Answers will vary.

© Evan-Moor Corp. • EMC 2754 • Language Fundamentals   Suffix *-less* 173

Page 174

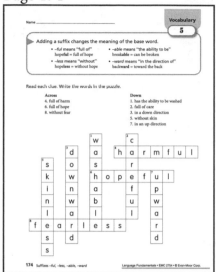

Name _____

Vocabulary 5

Adding a suffix changes the meaning of the base word.

– *-ful* means "full of"   – *-able* means "the ability to be"
  hopeful = full of hope   breakable = can be broken
– *-less* means "without"   – *-ward* means "in the direction of"
  hopeless = without hope   backward = toward the back

Read each clue. Write the words in the puzzle.

Across
4. full of harm
6. full of hope
8. without fear

Down
1. has the ability to be washed
2. full of care
3. in a down direction
5. without skin
7. in an up direction

Crossword answers: harmful, hopeful, fearless, downward, washable, careful, skinless, upward

174 Suffixes *-ful*, *-less*, *-able*, *-ward*   Language Fundamentals • EMC 2754 • © Evan-Moor Corp.

Page 175

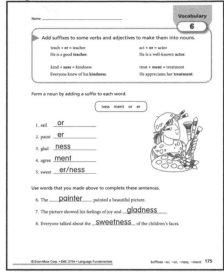

Name _____

Vocabulary 6

Add suffixes to some verbs and adjectives to make them into nouns.

teach + er = teacher   act + or = actor
He is a good **teacher**.   He is a well-known **actor**.

kind + ness = kindness   treat + ment = treatment
Everyone knew of his **kindness**.   He appreciates her **treatment**.

Form a noun by adding a suffix to each word.

ness   ment   or   er

1. sail   **or**
2. paint   **er**
3. glad   **ness**
4. agree   **ment**
5. sweet   **er/ness**

Use words that you made above to complete these sentences.

6. The **painter** painted a beautiful picture.
7. The picture showed his feelings of joy and **gladness**.
8. Everyone talked about the **sweetness** of the children's faces.

© Evan-Moor Corp. • EMC 2754 • Language Fundamentals   Suffixes *-er*, *-or*, *-ness*, *-ment* 175

Page 176

Name _____

Vocabulary Review 1

Fill in the bubble next to the correct answer.

1. What is the base word in *recharge*?
   Ⓐ re
   Ⓑ char
   ● charge
   Ⓓ rec

2. What is the prefix in *unhelpfully*?
   ● un
   Ⓑ help
   Ⓒ ful
   Ⓓ ly

3. Which word means "appear again"?
   ● reappear
   Ⓑ disappear
   Ⓒ preappear
   Ⓓ appeared

4. What is the suffix in *unsinkable*?
   Ⓐ un
   Ⓑ sink
   Ⓒ sinkable
   ● able

5. Which word means "without hope"?
   Ⓐ hoping
   Ⓑ hopeful
   ● hopeless
   Ⓓ hopefulness

176 Vocabulary: Review 1   Language Fundamentals • EMC 2754 • © Evan-Moor Corp.

Page 177

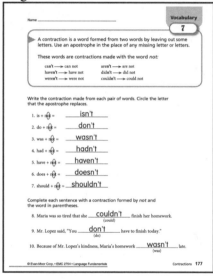

Name _____

Vocabulary 7

A contraction is a word formed from two words by leaving out some letters. Use an apostrophe in the place of any missing letter or letters.

These words are contractions made with the word *not*:

can't → can not   aren't → are not
haven't → have not   didn't → did not
weren't → were not   couldn't → could not

Write the contraction made from each pair of words. Circle the letter that the apostrophe replaces.

1. is + n(o)t = **isn't**
2. do + n(o)t = **don't**
3. was + n(o)t = **wasn't**
4. had + n(o)t = **hadn't**
5. have + n(o)t = **haven't**
6. does + n(o)t = **doesn't**
7. should + n(o)t = **shouldn't**

Complete each sentence with a contraction formed by *not* and the word in parentheses.

8. Maria was so tired that she **couldn't** finish her homework.
   (could)
9. Mr. Lopez said, "You **don't** have to finish today."
   (do)
10. Because of Mr. Lopez's kindness, Maria's homework **wasn't** late.
    (was)

© Evan-Moor Corp. • EMC 2754 • Language Fundamentals   Contractions 177

Page 178

Name _____

Vocabulary 8

Many contractions are made with forms of the verb *to be*.

I am → I'm   we are → we're
she is → she's   they are → they're
it is → it's   you are → you're

Complete the chart. The first one has been done for you.

Two Words	Contraction	What Apostrophe Replaces
1. he is	he's	i
2. you are	you're	a
3. they are	they're	a
4. it is	it's	i
5. I am	I'm	a
6. we are	we're	a

Write a contraction with a form of *to be* to complete each sentence.

7. The rain has stopped, and **it's** sunny outside.
8. The friends have decided that **they're** going to go to the beach.
9. Marlo and I agreed that **we're** going to the zoo Saturday.
10. When we got there, I said to Marlo, "**I'm** happy to see all the animals."

Answers may vary; suggested answers given.

178 Contractions   Language Fundamentals • EMC 2754 • © Evan-Moor Corp.

Page 179

Name _____

Vocabulary Review 2

Fill in the bubble next to the correct answer.

1. Which contraction is made from *could not*?
   Ⓐ can't
   Ⓑ cannot
   ● couldn't
   Ⓓ shouldn't

2. Which contraction is made from *it is*?
   ● it's
   Ⓑ I'm
   Ⓒ isn't
   Ⓓ hasn't

3. Which word correctly completes the sentence?
   The twins bought sleeping bags because ____ going camping.
   Ⓐ he's
   Ⓑ it's
   Ⓒ you're
   ● they're

4. Which word correctly completes the sentence?
   I love baseball, so ____ going to the game today.
   ● I'm
   Ⓑ It's
   Ⓒ I've
   Ⓓ Isn't

5. Which word correctly completes the sentence?
   We ____ seen any new movies lately.
   Ⓐ can't
   ● haven't
   Ⓒ aren't
   Ⓓ hasn't

© Evan-Moor Corp. • EMC 2754 • Language Fundamentals   Vocabulary: Review 2 179

Page 180

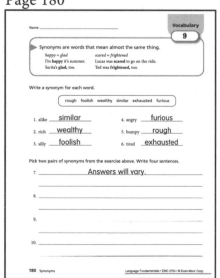

Name _____

Vocabulary 9

Synonyms are words that mean almost the same thing.

happy = glad   scared = frightened
I'm **happy** it's summer.   Lucas was **scared** to go on the ride.
Sarita's **glad**, too.   Ted was **frightened**, too.

Write a synonym for each word.

rough   foolish   wealthy   similar   exhausted   furious

1. alike   **similar**   4. angry   **furious**
2. rich   **wealthy**   5. bumpy   **rough**
3. silly   **foolish**   6. tired   **exhausted**

Pick two pairs of synonyms from the exercise above. Write four sentences.

7. Answers will vary.
8.
9.
10.

180 Synonyms   Language Fundamentals • EMC 2754 • © Evan-Moor Corp.

Page 181

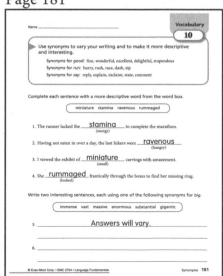

Name _____

Vocabulary 10

Use synonyms to vary your writing and to make it more descriptive and interesting.

Synonyms for *good*: fine, wonderful, excellent, delightful, stupendous
Synonyms for *run*: hurry, rush, race, dash, zip
Synonyms for *say*: reply, explain, exclaim, state, comment

Complete each sentence with a more descriptive word from the word box.

miniature   stamina   ravenous   rummaged

1. The runner lacked the **stamina** to complete the marathon.
   (energy)
2. Having not eaten in over a day, the lost hikers were **ravenous**.
   (hungry)
3. I viewed the exhibit of **miniature** carvings with amazement.
   (small)
4. She **rummaged** frantically through the boxes to find her missing ring.
   (looked)

Write two interesting sentences, each using one of the following synonyms for *big*.

immense   vast   massive   enormous   substantial   gigantic

5. Answers will vary.
6.

© Evan-Moor Corp. • EMC 2754 • Language Fundamentals   Synonyms 181

Page 182

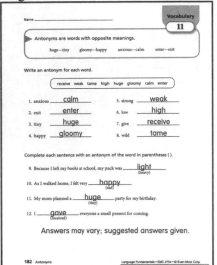

▶ Antonyms are words with opposite meanings.

huge—tiny   gloomy—happy   anxious—calm   enter—exit

Write an antonym for each word.

receive weak tame high huge gloomy calm enter

1. anxious __calm__
2. exit __enter__
3. tiny __huge__
4. happy __gloomy__
5. strong __weak__
6. low __high__
7. give __receive__
8. wild __tame__

Complete each sentence with an antonym of the word in parentheses ( ).

9. Because I left my books at school, my pack was __light__ (heavy)

10. As I walked home, I felt very __happy__ (sad)

11. My mom planned a __huge__ party for my birthday. (tiny)

12. I __gave__ everyone a small present for coming. (received)

Answers may vary; suggested answers given.

182 Antonyms   Language Fundamentals • EMC 2754 • © Evan-Moor Corp.

Page 183

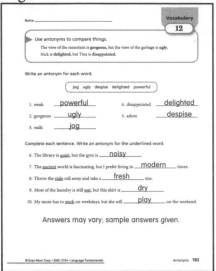

▶ Use antonyms to compare things.

The view of the mountain is **gorgeous**, but the view of the garbage is **ugly**.
Nick is **delighted**, but Tina is **disappointed**.

Write an antonym for each word.

jog ugly despise delighted powerful

1. weak __powerful__
2. gorgeous __ugly__
3. walk __jog__
4. disappointed __delighted__
5. adore __despise__

Complete each sentence. Write an antonym for the underlined word.

6. The library is quiet, but the gym is __noisy__.

7. The ancient world is fascinating, but I prefer living in __modern__ times.

8. Throw the stale roll away and take a __fresh__ one.

9. Most of the laundry is still wet, but this shirt is __dry__.

10. My mom has to work on weekdays, but she will __play__ on the weekend.

Answers may vary; sample answers given.

© Evan-Moor Corp. • EMC 2754 • Language Fundamentals   Antonyms 183

Page 184

▶ Homophones are words that sound alike but have different spellings and different meanings.

Did you **write** the **right** answer? I wrote "true" for number **four**.

Write a homophone for each word.

1. ant __aunt__
2. sent __cent__
3. new __knew__
4. write __right__
5. sew __so__
6. threw __through__
7. ate __eight__
8. no __know__
9. pair __pear__
10. here __hear__

Write the word that completes the sentence correctly.

11. You need to decide __whether__ you will go home or not. (weather, whether)

12. "We are __all ready__ to go to the store," I answered. (already, all ready)

Write two sentences using the homophones.

13. (piece) __Answers will vary.__

14. (peace) _____

184 Homophones   Language Fundamentals • EMC 2754 • © Evan-Moor Corp.

Page 185

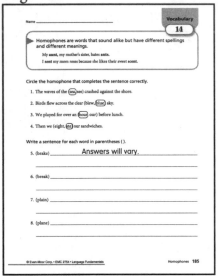

▶ Homophones are words that sound alike but have different spellings and different meanings.

My **aunt**, my mother's sister, hates **ants**.
I **sent** my mom roses because she likes their sweet **scent**.

Circle the homophone that completes the sentence correctly.

1. The waves of the (sea) see crashed against the shore.

2. Birds flew across the clear (blew, blue) sky.

3. We played for over an (hour, our) before lunch.

4. Then we (eight, ate) our sandwiches.

Write a sentence for each word in parentheses ( ).

5. (brake) __Answers will vary.__

6. (break) _____

7. (plain) _____

8. (plane) _____

© Evan-Moor Corp. • EMC 2754 • Language Fundamentals   Homophones 185

Page 186

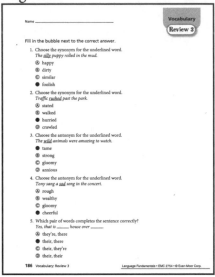

Fill in the bubble next to the correct answer.

1. Choose the synonym for the underlined word.
   The silly puppy rolled in the mud.
   Ⓐ happy
   Ⓑ dirty
   Ⓒ similar
   ● foolish

2. Choose the synonym for the underlined word.
   Traffic rushed past the park.
   Ⓐ stated
   Ⓑ walked
   ● hurried
   Ⓓ crawled

3. Choose the antonym for the underlined word.
   The wild animals were amazing to watch.
   ● tame
   Ⓑ strong
   Ⓒ gloomy
   Ⓓ anxious

4. Choose the antonym for the underlined word.
   Tony sang a sad song in the concert.
   Ⓐ rough
   Ⓑ wealthy
   Ⓒ gloomy
   ● cheerful

5. Which pair of words completes the sentence correctly?
   Yes, that is _____ house over _____.
   Ⓐ they're, there
   ● their, there
   Ⓒ there, they're
   Ⓓ their, their

186 Vocabulary: Review 3   Language Fundamentals • EMC 2754 • © Evan-Moor Corp.

Page 187

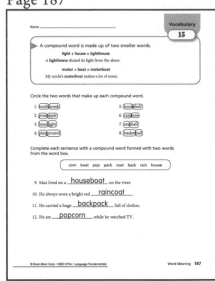

▶ A compound word is made up of two smaller words.

light + house = lighthouse
A **lighthouse** shined its light from the shore.

motor + boat = motorboat
My uncle's **motorboat** makes a lot of noise.

Circle the two words that make up each compound word.

1. tooth|brush
2. pine|apple
3. head|light
4. play|ground
5. book|shelf
6. rain|bow
7. sea|shell
8. basket|ball

Complete each sentence with a compound word formed with two words from the word box.

corn boat pop pack coat back rain house

9. Max lived on a __houseboat__ on the river.

10. He always wore a bright red __raincoat__.

11. He carried a huge __backpack__ full of clothes.

12. He ate __popcorn__ while he watched TV.

© Evan-Moor Corp. • EMC 2754 • Language Fundamentals   Word Meaning 187

Page 188

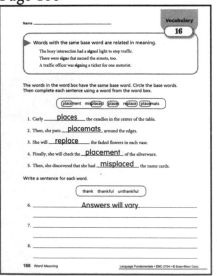

▶ Words with the same base word are related in meaning.

The busy intersection had a **signal** light to stop traffic.
There were **signs** that named the streets, too.
A traffic officer was **signing** a ticket for one motorist.

The words in the word box have the same base word. Circle the base words. Then complete each sentence using a word from the word box.

place|ment mis|placed place|s re|place place|mats

1. Carly __places__ the candles in the center of the table.

2. Then, she puts __placemats__ around the edges.

3. She will __replace__ the faded flowers in each vase.

4. Finally, she will check the __placement__ of the silverware.

5. Then, she discovered that she had __misplaced__ the name cards.

Write a sentence for each word.

thank thankful unthankful

6. __Answers will vary.__

7. _____

8. _____

188 Word Meaning   Language Fundamentals • EMC 2754 • © Evan-Moor Corp.

Page 189

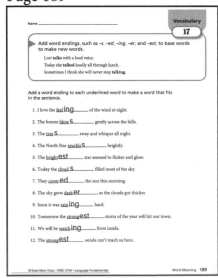

▶ Add word endings, such as –s, –ed, –ing, –er, and –est, to base words to make new words.

Lori **talks** with a loud voice.
Today she **talked** loudly all through lunch.
Sometimes I think she will never stop **talking**.

Add a word ending to each underlined word to make a word that fits in the sentence.

1. I love the feel__ing__ of the wind at night.

2. The breeze blow__s__ gently across the hills.

3. The tree__s__ sway and whisper all night.

4. The North Star sparkle__s__ brightly.

5. The bright__est__ star seemed to flicker and glow.

6. Today the cloud__s__ filled most of the sky.

7. They cover__ed__ the sun this morning.

8. The sky grew dark__er__ as the clouds got thicker.

9. Soon it was rain__ing__ hard.

10. Tomorrow the strong__est__ storm of the year will hit our town.

11. We will be watch__ing__ from inside.

12. The strong__est__ winds can't reach us here.

© Evan-Moor Corp. • EMC 2754 • Language Fundamentals   Word Meaning 189

Page 190

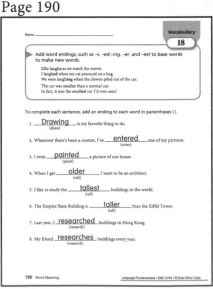

▶ Add word endings, such as –s, –ed, –ing, –er, and –est to base words to make new words.

Ellie laughs as we watch the movie.
I laughed when my cat pounced on a bug.
We were laughing when the clowns piled out of the car.
The car was smaller than a normal car.
In fact, it was the smallest car I'd ever seen!

To complete each sentence, add an ending to each word in parentheses ( ).

1. __Drawing__ is my favorite thing to do. (draw)

2. Whenever there's been a contest, I've __entered__ one of my pictures. (enter)

3. I even __painted__ a picture of our house. (paint)

4. When I get __older__ I want to be an architect. (old)

5. I like to study the __tallest__ buildings in the world. (tall)

6. The Empire State Building is __taller__ than the Eiffel Tower. (tall)

7. Last year, I __researched__ buildings in Hong Kong. (research)

8. My friend __researches__ buildings every year. (research)

190 Word Meaning   Language Fundamentals • EMC 2754 • © Evan-Moor Corp.

Page 191

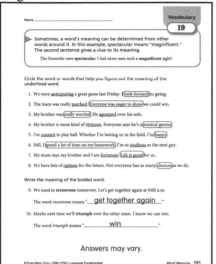

Vocabulary 19

Sometimes, a word's meaning can be determined from other words around it. In this example, *spectacular* means "magnificent." The second sentence gives a clue to its meaning.

The fireworks were **spectacular**. I had never seen such a *magnificent* sight!

Circle the word or words that help you figure out the meaning of the underlined word.

1. We were <u>anticipating</u> a great game last Friday. (look forward) to going.
2. The team was really <u>psyched.</u> (Everyone was eager to show) we could win.
3. My brother was (really worried) He <u>agonized</u> over his solo.
4. My brother is some kind of <u>virtuoso.</u> Everyone says he's a (musical genius)
5. I'm <u>content</u> to play ball. Whether I'm batting or in the field, I'm (happy)
6. Still, I (spend a lot of time on my homework.) I'm as <u>studious</u> as the next guy.
7. My mom says my brother and I are <u>fortunate.</u> (Life is good) for us.
8. We have lots of <u>options</u> for the future. Not everyone has as many (choices) as we do.

Write the meaning of the bolded word.

9. We need to **reconvene** tomorrow. Let's get together again at 9:00 a.m.

   The word *reconvene* means "___get together again___."

10. Maybe next time we'll **triumph** over the other team. I know we can win.

    The word *triumph* means "___win___."

Answers may vary.

© Evan-Moor Corp. • EMC 2754 • Language Fundamentals — Word Meaning **191**

Page 192

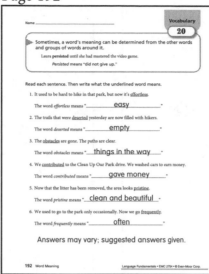

Vocabulary 20

Sometimes, a word's meaning can be determined from the other words and groups of words around it.

Laura **persisted** until she had mastered the video game.

Persisted means "did not give up."

Read each sentence. Then write what the underlined word means.

1. It used to be hard to hike in this park, but now it's <u>effortless.</u>

   The word *effortless* means "___easy___."

2. The trails that were <u>deserted</u> yesterday are now filled with hikers.

   The word *deserted* means "___empty___."

3. The <u>obstacles</u> are gone. The paths are clear.

   The word *obstacles* means "___things in the way___."

4. We <u>contributed</u> to the Clean Up Our Park drive. We washed cars to earn money.

   The word *contributed* means "___gave money___."

5. Now that the litter has been removed, the area looks <u>pristine.</u>

   The word *pristine* means "___clean and beautiful___."

6. We used to go to the park only occasionally. Now we go <u>frequently.</u>

   The word *frequently* means "___often___."

Answers may vary; suggested answers given.

192 Word Meaning — Language Fundamentals • EMC 2754 • © Evan-Moor Corp.

Page 193

Vocabulary Review 4

Fill in the bubble next to the correct answer.

1. Which of these words is a compound word?
   - Ⓐ fullness
   - Ⓑ brightest
   - Ⓒ fabulous
   - ● bookshelf

2. Mark the word that has the same base word as these words.
   thanks   thanked   thanking   thankless
   - Ⓐ tank
   - Ⓑ through
   - Ⓒ thinking
   - ● thankful

3. Which word completes the sentence correctly?
   Darren _____ whenever he is asked.
   - Ⓐ helps
   - Ⓑ helpful
   - Ⓒ helping
   - Ⓓ helper

4. Which word does *not* have the same base word as the others?
   - Ⓐ laughs
   - ● lampshade
   - Ⓒ laughing
   - Ⓓ laughed

5. Which word has a similar meaning to the underlined word?
   The clamor of the crowd was deafening.
   - ● noise
   - Ⓑ quiet
   - Ⓒ silliness
   - Ⓓ coughing

© Evan-Moor Corp. • EMC 2754 • Language Fundamentals — Vocabulary: Review 4 **193**

Page 195

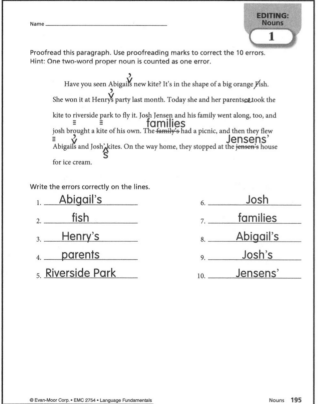

EDITING: Nouns 1

Proofread this paragraph. Use proofreading marks to correct the 10 errors.
Hint: One two-word proper noun is counted as one error.

Have you seen Abigails new kite? It's in the shape of a big orange Fish. She won it at Henrys party last month. Today she and her parents took the kite to riverside park to fly it. Josh Jensen and his family went along, too, and josh brought a kite of his own. The family's had a picnic, and then they flew Abigails and Josh' kites. On the way home, they stopped at the jensen's house for ice cream.

Write the errors correctly on the lines.

1. ___Abigail's___
2. ___fish___
3. ___Henry's___
4. ___parents___
5. ___Riverside Park___
6. ___Josh___
7. ___families___
8. ___Abigail's___
9. ___Josh's___
10. ___Jensens'___

© Evan-Moor Corp. • EMC 2754 • Language Fundamentals — Nouns **195**

Page 196

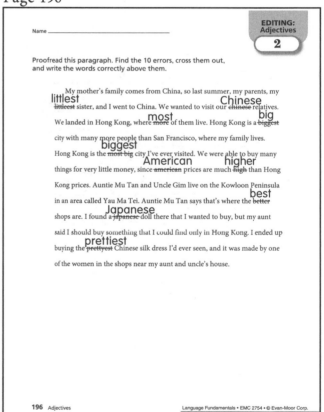

EDITING: Adjectives 2

Proofread this paragraph. Find the 10 errors, cross them out, and write the words correctly above them.

My mother's family comes from China, so last summer, my parents, my ~~littlest~~ **littlest** sister, and I went to China. We wanted to visit our ~~chinese~~ **Chinese** relatives. We landed in Hong Kong, where ~~more~~ **most** of them live. Hong Kong is a ~~biggest~~ **big** city with many more people than San Francisco, where my family lives. Hong Kong is the ~~most big~~ **biggest** city I've ever visited. We were able to buy many things for very little money, since ~~american~~ **American** prices are much ~~high~~ **higher** than Hong Kong prices. Auntie Mu Tan and Uncle Gim live on the Kowloon Peninsula in an area called Yau Ma Tei. Auntie Mu Tan says that's where the ~~better~~ **best** shops are. I found a ~~japanese~~ **Japanese** doll there that I wanted to buy, but my aunt said I should buy something that I could find only in Hong Kong. I ended up buying the ~~prettyest~~ **prettiest** Chinese silk dress I'd ever seen, and it was made by one of the women in the shops near my aunt and uncle's house.

196 Adjectives — Language Fundamentals • EMC 2754 • © Evan-Moor Corp.

Page 197

EDITING:
Adjectives

3

Proofread these paragraphs. Find the 10 errors. cross them out. and write the words correctly above them. Hint: A two-word proper adjective is counted as one error.

       many
There are ~~more~~ bodies of water in the United States. There are big bays
bigger   **biggest**
and ~~biger~~ lakes. The oceans on both sides of the country are the two ~~bigger~~
        largest
oceans on Earth. The Pacific Ocean is the ~~larger~~ ocean in the world. The
      smaller   **largest**
Atlantic Ocean is ~~small~~ than the Pacific, but it is the second-~~larger~~ ocean
on Earth.
              longest
     The Missouri is the ~~most long~~ river in the United States. However, the
Egyptian   **South American**   **Chinese**
~~egypt~~ river the Nile, the ~~south american~~ river the Amazon, and the ~~chinese~~
river the Yangtze are longer.

Page 198

EDITING:
Pronouns

4

Proofread this paragraph. Use proofreading marks to correct the 10 errors.

     Philippe is a new student in our class. He comes from Lyon, a town in
                         they
France. His family is French, but ~~them~~ speak English very well. Philippe's
                        My family and I
                 he   **my**
father is a chef in a French restaurant here. ~~Me and my family~~ have eaten
               me   **My sister and I**
there twice because ~~they~~ started working there. Mom orders for Dad, ~~mine~~
sister, and ~~I~~ because she can say the names of the dishes. ~~Me and my sister~~
ordered the same thing both times. I can't say the French name yet, but it's
                         My   **she**
called Lamb in Parsley in English. ~~My's~~ mom told my sister ~~her~~ didn't have
to eat it all if she didn't like it. My sister ate every last bite of her's. So did I!

Write the errors correctly on the lines.

1. ___**our**___   6. ___**me**___
2. ___**they**___   7. ___**My sister and I**___
3. ___**My family and I**___   8. ___**My**___
4. ___**he**___   9. ___**she**___
5. ___**my**___   10. ___**hers**___

Page 199

EDITING:
Pronouns

5

Proofread these paragraphs. Find the 10 errors. cross them out. and write the words correctly above them.

                He and she/They
     Caleb and Jenny are best friends. ~~Him and her~~ do everything together.
                               her
When Caleb signed up for swimming lessons, Jenny sent in ~~hers~~ application.
                                 her
When Jenny started helping Mrs. Toyama clean up ~~his~~ yard, Caleb jumped
                        they
right in to help. Every Saturday, ~~their~~ help Mrs. Toyama for a couple of
   She
hours. ~~Her~~ has a huge yard, and now that her kids are grown, she needs help
      it
keeping ~~them~~ up.
     Jenny mows the lawn usually. Caleb pulls weeds and trims the bushes.
He
~~She~~ takes breaks when he gets tired and talks to Mrs. Toyama about her life
        She
back in Japan. ~~Her~~ and her husband moved to Chicago 45 years ago to go to
college. Dr. Toyama is retired now and has health problems. Sometimes
          he
when he feels up to it, ~~they~~ joins Caleb, Jenny, and Mrs. Toyama on the
        Their
porch for tea and cookies. ~~They're~~ time together is always interesting.

Page 200

EDITING:
Verbs

6

Proofread these paragraphs. Find the 10 errors. cross them out. and write the words correctly above them.

          wanted   **lived**
     Kaya had always ~~want~~ a horse, but she and her family ~~live~~ in a house with
                    begged
a small backyard. No matter how much Kaya ~~beged~~ her mother for a horse,
        was   **talking**
the answer ~~were~~ always the same: No room! One day at school, Kaya was ~~talk~~
              loves
to her teacher about how much she ~~love~~ horses.
     "I love horses, too," Ms. Nakai said. "That's why I volunteer at Kids for
         is   **Do**
Horses. It ~~was~~ a group that helps kids and horses help each other. ~~Does~~ you
want to find out more about it?"
                      replied   **became**
     "That would be great," Kaya ~~replyed~~. And that's how Kaya ~~becomed~~ an
active volunteer at Kids for Horses, helping many horses find families to take
good care of them.

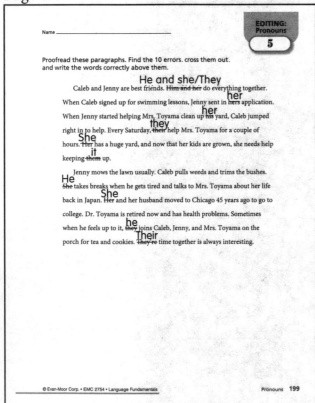

Page 201

Name _____

EDITING:
Verbs
7

Proofread this paragraph. Use proofreading marks to correct the 10 errors.

    studied
    Have you ever ~~studyed~~ the living things you can find at the seashore?

are   have
There ~~is~~ sea urchins, crabs, sea horses, and sand dollars. I ~~has~~ always loved

watching the crabs. They are so funny, with the way they walk∧ and their
                    es   have
funny legs. My whole family watch∧ them when we go to the beach. We ~~has~~

a contest to see who can find the most crabs. My sister Carrie found∧ the

most the last time we went. The next visit, I will ~~have been~~ the one to find the
    broke   be
most. Carrie ~~breaked~~ my dad's record of 15, but I'm going to break∧ hers.

Write the errors correctly on the lines.

1.   studied   6.   have
2.   are   7.   found
3.   have   8.   be
4.   walk   9.   broke
5.   watches   10.   break

Page 202

Name _____

EDITING:
Verbs
8

Proofread these paragraphs. Find the 10 errors, cross them out, and write the words correctly above them.

        was
    Olivia ~~were~~ so frustrated! She had studied all week for the test in
           read   went
Language Arts. She ~~readed~~ the book twice and then ~~go~~ over it again and
                                memorized
again, thinking about what might be on the test. She ~~memorizes~~ the names of
               wrote
the people in the story. She ~~write~~ questions about the book and answered
      had
them. She ~~haved~~ her brother Jamie quiz her on the main themes in the story.
      got   felt
    When Olivia ~~gotten~~ to school on Friday, she ~~feeled~~ good. When she
    couldn't
started the test, she ~~can't~~ believe her eyes. She had studied the wrong book!
              told
Mr. Kerman was so nice about it. He ~~telled~~ Olivia she could retake the test

the next week.

Page 203

Name _____

EDITING:
Verbs
9

Proofread these paragraphs. Use proofreading marks to correct the 10 errors.

    Graciela was the best soccer player in fifth grade at her school. She want∧ed

to be the best fifth-grade player in the county, so she practiced every day after
          practiced   did
school. Sometimes she ~~practice~~ with her team, and sometimes she ~~do~~ it on

her own.
         going
    The next game was ~~go~~ well, until Graciela slipped in the mud on the
    fell   cried   hit
field and ~~falled~~. "Ow!" she ~~cryed~~ as she ~~hitted~~ the ground. Everyone rushed

over to check on Graciela. "I'm OK," she said as she slowly got∧ up.
                                was
After she rested on the bench for a while, Graciela ~~is~~ ready to go back into
          kicked
the game. That day, she ~~kick~~ the winning goal. She was finally the best player

in the county.

Write the errors correctly on the lines.

1.   wanted   6.   cried
2.   practiced   7.   hit
3.   did   8.   got
4.   going   9.   was
5.   fell   10.   kicked

Page 204

Name _____

EDITING:
Adverbs
10

Proofread this paragraph. Use proofreading marks to correct the 10 errors.

               happily
    I can't listen to Irish fiddle music without ~~happy~~ tapping my feet. My

Aunt Maura has played the fiddle for a very long time, and she plays very
well   ly
~~good~~. She performs regular∧ at Celtic music festivals. People crowd eager∧ near
                                 ly
the stage to watch the fiddlers in action. There are usual∧ dancers on stage,
                         quicker
too. The faster the fiddlers play, the ~~quicklier~~ the dancers dance. I'm studying

Irish step dancing. I want to dance ~~more~~ better than my sister, Colleen, but

that's going to take practice. I've ~~not~~ never seen a better dancer than Colleen,

but someday people will be singing my praises loud∧ too!

Write the errors correctly on the lines.

1.   happily   6.   usually
2.   very   7.   quicker
3.   well   8.   better
4.   regularly   9.   not or never
5.   eagerly   10.   loudly

Page 205

EDITING:
Sentences
11

Name _____

Proofread this paragraph. Correct the incomplete sentences by adding words to make them complete. Write the corrected paragraph on the lines below.

What's your favorite National Park? Mine Yosemite. Our first time there we camped in the valley. We El Capitan from almost everywhere. Is like a big stone mountain. Looks as if half of it has been cut away. The next time we stayed in Tuolumne Meadows, which is a big open field. Yosemite is beautiful, whichever way you see it.

(inserted: is, could see, we, It, It)

Answers will vary. Accept any complete sentences that make sense.

© Evan-Moor Corp. • EMC 2754 • Language Fundamentals   Sentences **205**

Page 206

EDITING:
Sentences
12

Name _____

Find each run-on sentence and correct it. You can create two sentences or make the run-on sentence into a compound or complex sentence, using conjunctions. Write the corrected paragraph on the lines below.

Have you ever seen a tornado heading your way it's a very scary sight!

The tornado looks like a big, dark funnel tornadoes can happen anywhere in the U.S. about 1,000 tornadoes are reported from all over the country every year. A tornado can travel at speeds up to 250 miles per hour or more it can cause damage in a path that is up to a mile wide and 50 miles long. You should research what to do in case of a tornado you will know what to do. Be prepared stay safe.

(inserted marks: ? , and , and so , and)

Answers may vary; sample answers given.

206 Sentences   Language Fundamentals • EMC 2754 • © Evan-Moor Corp.

Page 207

EDITING:
Sentences
13

Name _____

Read the paragraph and then rewrite it on the lines below to make it read more smoothly. Combine sentences to avoid choppiness and unnecessary repetition.

Lucy was an only child. Lucy had been an only child for six years. One day, her parents told her something. They told her that she was going to have a baby brother. Everyone in the family was really excited. They were excited about the baby. Lucy wasn't sure. She wasn't sure about having a little brother. Then one day her parents went to the hospital. They went there to have the baby. Lucy went to the hospital the next day. She got to hold the baby. The baby was fussing. Lucy started to hum to him. He stopped crying. Having a little brother might be pretty cool after all!

Answers will vary; sample answer given.

Lucy was an only child for six years. One day her parents told her that she was going to have a baby brother. Everyone in the family was really excited about the baby, but Lucy wasn't sure about having a little brother. Then one day her parents went to the hospital to have the baby. When Lucy went to the hospital the next day, she got to hold the baby. The baby was fussing. When Lucy started to hum to him, he stopped crying. Having a little brother might be pretty cool after all!

© Evan-Moor Corp. • EMC 2754 • Language Fundamentals   Sentences **207**

Page 208

EDITING:
Capitalization
14

Name _____

Proofread this paragraph. Use proofreading marks to correct the 10 errors.

My brother juan and I love to watch old movies, and I mean really old movies! My brother is 12 and I'm 10, but we watch movies that were made before my parents were born! Juan likes the dance movies with fred Astaire, who was a famous movie star in the 1930s and 1940s. I like musicals, too, and my favorite is called West Side story. My birthday is in march, and Juan bought me a DVD. it's called Funny face, and it stars Fred Astaire and audrey Hepburn. Audrey Hepburn is one of my favorite actresses. My birthday was on a saturday, so Juan and I stayed up late and watched the movie. Juan's birthday is august 23. There is a festival of old movies in New york City on that day, so we're going to go for his birthday.

Write the errors correctly on the lines.

1. Juan
2. Fred/Fred Astaire
3. Story/West Side Story
4. March
5. It's
6. Face/Funny Face
7. Audrey/Audrey Hepburn
8. Saturday
9. August
10. York/New York City

208 Capitalization   Language Fundamentals • EMC 2754 • © Evan-Moor Corp.

EDITING:
Punctuation
15

Name _____

Proofread these paragraphs. Correct any errors and add any missing punctuation.

Mina's Aunt Farida is teaching Mina and her brother, Badri, to cook. Aunt Farida is known throughout the neighborhood for her fantastic cooking! or .

Mina loves fish, chicken, and lamb, so her aunt is teaching her how to make some special dishes for each type of meat. Badri's favorite dishes are made with vegetables because he doesn't eat meat. Aunt Farida taught him to make a dish that calls for 450 g. of green beans! That sounds like a lot, but it's really only 1 lb. Mina likes chili peppers, but Badri doesn't like his food too hot.

Do you know what the best part of a cooking lesson is? You get to eat everything you cook!

Write the corrected second paragraph on the lines below.
Remember to include the correct punctuation.

Mina loves fish, chicken, and lamb, so her aunt is teaching her how to make some special dishes for each type of meat. Badri's favorite dishes are made with vegetables because he doesn't eat meat. Aunt Farida taught him to make a dish that calls for 450 g of green beans! That sounds like a lot, but it's really only 1 lb. Mina likes chili peppers, but Badri doesn't like his food too hot.

EDITING:
Punctuation
16

Name _____

Proofread these paragraphs. Correct any errors and add any missing punctuation.

Darrell and his mother were meeting Darrell's father at Grand Central Station. They had just moved to New York, and they weren't familiar with the station. Mrs. Williams went up to the information window. "Excuse me," she asked the woman in the booth. "Can you tell me when the train from White Plains arrives?"

"The next one is due in at 4:17 on Track 19," she replied.

"Where is that?" asked Mrs. Williams.

"Right over there," the woman replied, pointing to the stairs leading to the track.

They looked at where the woman was pointing, and there was Darrell's father coming up the stairs. It was a happy reunion for all!

Write the corrected first paragraph on the lines below.
Remember to include the correct punctuation.

Darrell and his mother were meeting Darrell's father at Grand Central Station. They had just moved to New York, and they weren't familiar with the station. Mrs. Williams went up to the information window. "Excuse me," she asked the woman in the booth. "Can you tell me when the train from White Plains arrives?"

EDITING:
Punctuation
17

Name _____

Proofread this paragraph. Correct any errors and add any missing punctuation.

After school lets out at 2:45, Elena and Rodrigo help Mr. Wey shelve books in the school library. They help sort the books, and then they put the books on shelves where they belong. They also put magazines, newspapers, and paperbacks where they belong. Why do they work in the library? They both like to read, and this way they get to see the latest books when they come in. Elena's favorite book is A Wrinkle in Time by Madeleine L'Engle. Rodrigo's favorite book is Breaking Through by Francisco Jiménez.

Write the paragraph correctly on the lines below.
Remember to include all of your corrections.

Paragraphs should reflect the corrections shown above.

_____

_____

_____

_____

_____

_____

_____

_____

EDITING:
Punctuation
18

Name _____

Proofread this business letter. Correct any errors and add any missing punctuation marks.

Lourdes Posadas
47 79th Street
Allentown, pa

May 7, 2007

Wendell Sporting Goods
171 Randall Ave.
Kansas City, MO

To Whom It May Concern:

I purchased a Frost Proof parka at your store on April 16, 2007, and I would like to bring something to your attention. The tag on the parka said that the jacket was waterproof. I wore the jacket in a rainstorm the week after I bought it, and I got soaked!

I am returning the jacket, and I would appreciate a refund of the $97.99 that I paid for it. Please send it to the address above. Thank you for your help with this.

Sincerely,

Lourdes Posadas

Name _____

Read these paragraphs. Cross out any errors and correct them above the crossed out words.

Geri is a wonderful artist. She has been drawing since she could hold a crayon. Geri doesn't know ~~nothing~~ *anything* about sports, but she can tell you everything about ~~a~~ *an* ancient painter called Giotto. Giotto painted something called "frescos," or paintings on walls. ~~Its~~ *It's* amazing how they've lasted over the centuries. Geri paints very ~~good~~ *well* herself. ~~Their~~ *There* are many galleries that show her paintings.

Geri says, "You have to follow ~~you're~~ *your* heart and do what you love. ~~Were~~ *We're* always rushing around, trying to succeed. The way to succeed is to do what makes you happy."

Geri knows that if you do what matters ~~too~~ *to* you, you'll do it ~~good~~ *well*. ~~Its~~ *It's* what is in your heart that's important," she says.

Name _____

Proofread these paragraphs. Find the 10 errors, cross them out, and write the words correctly above them.

Carter plays baseball really ~~good~~ *well*. ~~They're~~ *There* is nothing he likes better than batting the ball around. He and his sister, Alexis, love to play in ~~there~~ *their* backyard. Carter hits, while Alexis catches. There isn't ~~nobody~~ *anybody* in the Roseville Kids' League who catches better than Alexis. She can catch ~~an~~ *a* fly ball from anywhere in the field.

On Wednesday, the Kids' League sent out ~~it's~~ *its* list for the All-Star Game. ~~Your~~ *You're* not going to believe what happened," Carter told Alex. "Both of us have been chosen to play in the All-Star Game. This ~~is well~~ *good* for both of us," he continued.

~~Were~~ *We're* going to get a chance to show everyone how good we are," Alexis said. "That's what teamwork will do for you. ~~Its~~ *It's* great to get to do this together!"